COMPUTING WITH
THE SCIENTIFIC CALCULATOR

© 1986 CASIO, INC.

CASIO.

PREFACE

The unique capabilities of the scientific calculator can benefit engineers, scientists, business people, students, and many others. These calculators are widely available because of their relatively low cost. Many users of the hand-held scientific calculator do not use this incredible device to its fullest potential. This book will help the reader obtain the maximum benefit from the scientific calculator.

The examples included in this book have been selected to illustrate a wide variety of solution techniques. The reader should follow through these examples, even if the subject matter may not be of direct concern.

The book covers function keys that may not be found on all calculators. In some cases, alternative means of solution are suggested. Otherwise, the reader may skip the example. Unique time-saving techniques provided by scientific calculators are used in many places. The specific technique of using each key is given in detail in the first part of the book. Detailed applications in Math, Statistics, Physics, Electronics, Engineering, and Business follow in Part Two.

Two indexes are provided. One is standard type; the other is by function key only. Photographs accompanying the text at various points illustrate the actual display to aid the reader in understanding the results.

Your comments and suggestions for future editions would be welcomed.

CONTENTS

PART I: Basics

PART III: Programming Notes

APPENDIX

INDEX

Chapter 1 **Introduction**

Algebraic Logic

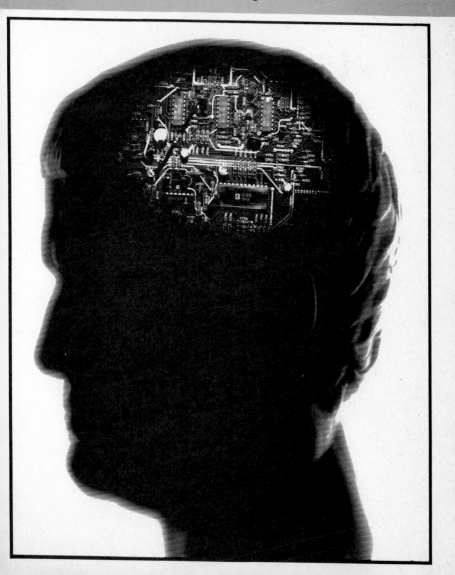

Introduction

Calculators were limited to the basic mathematical functions of addition, subtraction, multiplication and division until the early 1970's. The development of the electronic miracle, the semiconductor chip using large scale integration, allowed the programming of a wide variety of functions into a small hand-held calculator.

The scientific calculator came into being and opened a whole new world of computing power. This new type of calculator has eliminated the once common mathematical tool known as the slide rule by taking over all of its jobs. At the same time, the scientific calculator also did away with the need for the cumbersome tables of trigonometric and logarithmic functions. By employing the proper technique, the scientific calculator can be used in place of mortgage and loan tables.

Another major advance of recent years has been the incorporation of "solar" cells into most scientific calculators, eliminating the need for batteries. Very low levels of light will operate your calculator.

*   All keystroke functions used in the examples are shown with a box. Numbers and the decimal point are not boxed. The need to press the inverse key before a function varies from calculator to calculator. The reader will press inverse, where required, before a function key, even if it is not indicated in the text.*

Algebraic Logic

In developing the method for solving a problem with a scientific calculator, it is important to remember the basic algebraic approach to calculating. True algebraic logic means that in a series of operations, multiplication and division will be carried out before addition and subtraction.

The strategy for solving the expression:

$18 - 2 \times 4 =$ is to place the expression into the calculator exactly as you would read it. The answer is 10 because 2 is multiplied by 4 first and the result 8, is subtracted from 18 to get the answer.

True algebraic logic applies to mathematical problems whether or not a calculator is used. All calculations in this book assume the use of calculators with true algebraic logic. The majority of scientific calculators available today follow this pattern of operations.

All functions on the scientific calculator are performed in a specified sequence of priorities. Each function has a priority which may effect the strategy used in solving a particular problem. A table of priorities is given in the Appendix.

Parentheses are used as part of the technique when the solution to the problem requires that the calculator's built-in priorities be disregarded.

Chapter 2 **Function Keys**

Addition & Subtraction

Casio scientific calculators use floating-point numbers. The decimal place is automatically placed at the appropriate location, as in the following example:

Add: 4.11, .0002, 12, and 300

Key in: *Answer:*

4.11 ⊞ .0002 ⊞ 12 ⊞ 300 ⊟   316.1102

```
DEG
  316.1102
```

Note: *All calculations (except binary, octal, and hexadecimal) are carried out in the "DEC" or "COMP" mode —* [MODE] [0]. *Each time one of the four basic function keys are pressed, a subtotal is given on the display.*

Subtract from 100: .111, 50, 10, and 40

Key in: *Answer:*

100 ⊟ .111 ⊟ 50 ⊟ 10 ⊟ 40 ⊟   −0.111

Note: *When the answer is a negative, the number in the display is preceded by a minus sign.*

The calculator display is limited to 8 or 10 digits and only the most significant digits in a calculation will be retained. Care must be taken to avoid errors if answers with more than 10-digit accuracy are required.

Addition & Subtraction

10-digit Examples:

Add: 1234567890, .0011, and .22

Key in:	Displayed Answer:
1234567890 ⊞ .0011 ⊞ .22 ⊟	**1234567890.**

Subtract: 1234567890 from the above answer.

Key in:	Answer:
⊟ 1234567890 ⊟	**0.2**

Note: *Even though a 10-digit answer is displayed, eleven digits are carried internally by the calculator.*

Multiplication & Division

A computer has a random access memory (RAM) size of 64K bytes (1K is 1024 bytes). The user wishes to store 4-16,500 byte programs in the computer simultaneously. Will there be enough room?

Key in:	Answer (total storage required)
4 ☒ 16500 ▣	**66,000 bytes**
➗ 1024 ▣	**64.453 K bytes**

The answer is greater than the 64K available for internal storage. Therefore, the 4 programs will not fit on the computer.

An inventory consists of 25 items valued at $256.86, 17 at $56.82, and 279 at $6.40. Calculate the total value of the inventory.

Key in:	Answer:
25 ☒ 256.86 ⊞ 17 ☒ 56.82 ⊞ 279 ☒ 6.4 ▣	**$9173.04**

Note: *The calculator uses algebraic logic. Multiplication and division take precedence over addition and subtraction.*

DEG
9173.04

Constants

Pressing a basic function twice after an initial entry will establish a constant and the symbol K will appear in the display.

Add 64K bytes to 8, 64, 128, and 256K bytes of memory.

Key in:	Answer:
64 ⊞ ⊞ 8 ▭	72
64 ▭	128
128 ▭	192
256 ▭	320

```
  K DEG
            320.
```

The initial entry can be used to establish a table of values.

Key in:	Answer:
64 ⊞ ⊞	64
▭	128
▭	192
▭	256

Deduct 64 from each of the above answers.

Key in:	Answer:
64 ⊟ ⊟ 64 ▭	0
128 ▭	64
192 ▭	128
256 ▭	192
▭	(double deduction) 128

What are the actual number of bytes in 64K, 128K, and 256K computers?

Key in:	Answer:
1024 ⊠ ⊠ 64 ▭	65536
128 ▭	131072
256 ▭	262144

Constants

The first number in multiplication can be used to construct a multiples table. Where does the value of K, 1024 come from?

Key in:	Answer	Computer Term
2 ☒ ☒ 1 ▭	2	2 bits
▭	4	nibble
▭	8	byte
▭	16	word
▭	32	
▭	64	
▭	128	
▭	256	
▭	512	
▭	1024	kilobyte

The initial entry establishing a constant can be a calculation.

Key in:	Answer:
512 ☒ 2 ▭ ▭ 65536 ▭	64
131072 ▭	128
262144 ▭	256

A constant divisor can be used to establish index numbers.

Average daily sales on the New York Stock exchange were: 1980 — 14,500,000; 1981 — 13,900,000; 1982 — 15,100,000; and 1983 — 14,900,000. Show these figures as index numbers using 1980 as a base.

Note: *The last 5 digits from each number are unnecessary.*

Key in:	Index #	Year
	100	1980
145 ▭ ▭ 139 ▭	96	1981
151 ▭	104	1982
149 ▭	103	1983

Parenthesis

The customary order of arithmetic operations followed by the calculator's use of algebraic logic may be overridden by the use of parenthesis. A group of calculations are clustered together by using the open parenthesis key. The functions within that pair of parenthesis are completed by pressing the close parenthesis key. 18* pairs of parenthesis may be opened before the first set is closed. Each time a new set is opened, the number of that set will appear in the display. If an attempt is made to open more than the number of permitted pairs of parenthesis, the error symbol E will appear in the right hand side of the display. Parenthesis may be opened six times following open and closed parenthesis within the same calculation.

* Depends on calculator model

Calculate: A $\dfrac{256 + 512 + 32}{1024 + 64 + 16}$

Calculate: B $1024 \times \dfrac{(512 + 64)/(1024 + 64) + 32 \times 4}{512 \times (-8)}$

Note: *Parenthesis are used to separate the numerator portion from the denominator.*

$(256 + 512 + 32) \div (1024 + 64 + 16)$

Note: *Parenthesis that occur at the beginning or end of a calculation need not be entered on the calculator.*

Key in: **Answer:**

256 ⊞ 512 ⊞ 32 ⊐ ÷ ⊏ 1024 ⊞
64 ⊞ 16 ⊟   0.7246

Note: *In a series of parentheses, the innermost pair of parenthesis will be calculated first.*

Key in: **Answer:**

1024 ⊠ ⊏ ⊏ 512 ⊞ 64 ⊐ ÷ ⊏
1024 ⊞ 64 ⊐ ⊞ 32 ⊠ 4 ⊐ ÷ ⊏
512 ⊠ 8 ⊬ ⊟   −32.132

Percent

The decimal equivalent of a number multiplied by 100 is the percent or the ratio to 1. For example, the number 50 (or 50.0) is 50 times greater than one or 5000% of 1. One half or 0.5 is the same as 50%. The percent key is an operator and does not require the use of the equals key.

The percent key can be used to find:

a. A part of a whole
b. The percent that one number represents of a total
c. The percent change.
d. The total given a number and percent

In 1983, 95,600 portable computers were purchased. 32% of the total were produced by Procomp. How many is that?

Key in: **Answer:**

95600 ⨯ 32 %   **30,592**

18,942 of the portable computers were produced by Comprof. What was Comprof's percentage of the total?

Key in: **Answer:**

18942 ÷ 95600 %   **19.8%**

In 1984, sales of portable computers increased to 250,000. What is the percent increase?

Note: *A problem of this nature is usually carried out by using the equation:*

$$\frac{B - A}{A} \times 100$$

or

$$\frac{250 - 95.6}{95.6} \times 100$$

Percent

The change is calculated automatically with the percent key.

Key in:	Answer:
250 ⊟ **95.6** %	**161.5% increase**

If the MBC portable sales of 175,000 units accounts for 33% of sales in 1985, what would be the total number sold?

Key in:	Answer:
175000 ÷ **33** %	**530,303**

Memory

The memory on a calculator is similar to a single storage register on a computer. One item can be stored on the calculator with a limit of ten digits for the mantissa, and 2 digits for the exponent.

The value in the calculator memory can be added to, subtracted from, or exchanged with a value in the display. **M** appears on the display when a value is being retained in memory.

[M+] and [M−] are operators and can be used instead of [=]. [Min] replaces the value in memory with the value in the display. [x↔M] places the value in memory, and, at the same time, places the memory amount in the display. [MR] recalls the value in the memory.

Memory is particularly useful where it is necessary to record interim values as in an inventory. A Computer store has a stock of 22 MBC-PC at a cost of $2250 each; 15 Pear IIe at $875; and 35 FOX-80 printers at $412. What is the value of the inventory? What is the value if 3 MBC-PC and 5 FOX-80 are sold?

Key in:	Answer:
[0] [Min]	
22 [×] 2250 [M+]	49500
15 [×] 875 [M+]	13125
35 [×] 412 [M+]	14420
[MR]	Total 1 77045
3 [×] 2250 [M−]	6750
5 [×] 412 [M−]	2060
[MR]	Total 2 68235

```
  M   DEG
           68235.
```

Memory

A computer owner has $100 available to spend on supplies. The owner purchases 2 ribbons at $5.95, 15 diskettes at $4.25, and a disk drive cleaner at $15.95. Will the $100 cover these expenditures?

Key in: **Answer:**

100 [Min]
2 [×] 5.95 [M−]
15 [×] 4.25 [M−]
15.95 [M−]
[MR]   **$8.40 remaining**

Exchange

The exchange key is primarily used in polar coordinate conversions. It can be used to determine the ratio of one item to a total.

A computer store sells 36 MBC-PC's, 19 Pear IIe's, and 6 HAL 2001 computers. What proportion is Pear of the total?

Key in: **Answer:**

36 [+] 19 [+] 6 [)] [÷] 19 [x↔y] [=]   **0.311**

Exponential

The number shown in the calculator display is limited to 10 digits. Exponential (scientific notation) is a shorthand method of writing very small or very large numbers, simplifying many types of complicated calculations. The results of a calculation will automatically be expressed exponentially if the answer exceeds 9,999,999,999 or is less than 0.000000001 (in the case of a 10 digit calculator).

A number expressed exponentially is divided between a mantissa and a two-digit exponent. The exponent value ranges between 10^{99} and 10^{-99}. A negative exponent indicates a string of zeros after the decimal point.

Enter:

Number		Mantissa		Exponent	Key in:
a)	84,200	= 8.42	×	10^4	8.42 [EXP] 4
b)	9,999 billion	= 9.999	×	10^{12}	9.999 [EXP] 12
c)	0.00000000000123	= 1.23	×	10^{-12}	1.23 [EXP] 12 [+/−]
d)	1,000	= 1	×	10^3	1 [EXP] 3
e)	80,000,000	= 8	×	10^7	8 [EXP] 7
f)	0.000001	= 1	×	10^{-6}	1 [EXP] 6 [+/−]

Multiply b by c:

Key in:	*Answer:*
9.999 [EXP] 12 [×] 1.23 [EXP] 12 [+/−] [=]	12.29877

Divide d by f:

Key in:	*Answer:*
1 [EXP] 3 [÷] 1 [EXP] 6 [+/−] [=]	1×10^9 or 1000000000

Exponential

Add d to e:

Key in: **Answer:**

1 EXP 3 + 8 EXP 7 =   80001000.

Add a to b:

Key in: **Answer:**

8.42 EXP 4 + 9.999 EXP 12 = 9.999×10^{12}

In addition or subtraction, if the answer will exceed the limits previously expressed and the exponent values are different, an answer will be obtained which is meaningless (the largest value entered).

```
DEG
9.999000084  12
```

Rounding Techniques

A calculator normally operates under a system known as "free floating decimal". As many decimal places will be shown in the display as required by an answer or as will fit in the display. On calculators with a **NORM** mode the number displayed can be brought back to the free floating decimal condition, if the calculator has been previously operated in one of three rounding modes.

The last number in the display will be rounded up or down under normal operation.

Divide: 20 by 3 and 10 by 3.

Key in: **Answer:**

    20 ÷ 3 =   6.666666667
    10 ÷ 3 =   3.333333333

The FIX key permits the rounding of any decimal from 0 to 8 digits (6 on an 8-digit calculator). Rounding will continue until the NORM key is used.

The FIX mode effects the display only. The numbers for internal calculations are not rounded off maintaining accuracy as indicated in the example below.

Key in: **Answer:**

    FIX 2
    1.99 ÷ 12 =   0.17
    NORM   0.1658333
    FIX 2   0.17
    X 12 =   1.99
    .17 X 12 =   2.04

```
 DEG        FIX
               2.04
```

Rounding Techniques

Note: *The* SCI *mode followed by 1 to 8 will result in the rounding of the mantissa to the given number of digits. Use of the* SCI *mode also means that the results of all calculations will be given in scientific notation. Use of the* NORM *mode after a result has been obtained will expand an answer to the full number of decimal places within the display capacity of the calculator.*

Using the RND rounding key after FIX or SCI have been established will round the number in the display to the number of places already specified. If a FIX of 3 is in use and 2.56789 is entered, the number will be reduced to 2.568 if RND is pressed.

The ENG key cannot be used to permanently set the calculator in engineering notation but will convert the exponent of an answer to a multiple of 3. Engineering notation is useful for reading an answer to standard metric or U.S. dimensions.

Examples:
a) *The conversion factor for miles to meters is 1609. How many kilometers is 20,000 miles?*

Note: *Set the* SCI *for 3-decimal place accuracy. The exponential value of 3 will represent the number of kilometers. If the exponential value in the answer is not a multiple of 3, press* ENG.

Key in:	Display	Answer:
SCI 4	0.000 00	
20000 ✕ 1609 =	3.218 07	
ENG	32.18 06	32,180,000

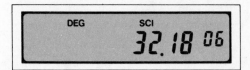

DEG   SCI
32.18 06

Rounding Techniques

b) Multiply 2,000 by 50,000 and read the answer.

Note: *If the exponential of the answer is not a multiple of 3, it will be difficult to read. Change to engineering notation. Remember 10^3 = thousand, 10^6 = million, 10^9 = billion.*

Key in:	Display	Answer:
[NORM] 2000 [×] 50000 [=]	1. 08 or 100000000.	
[ENG]	100. 06	100 million

Illustrate the metric scale for meters using the [ENG] key.

Key in:	Display	Read
1 [ENG]	1. 00	1 meter
[ENG]	1000. − 03	1000 millimeters
[ENG]	1000000. − 06	1000000 micrometers
[←ENG]	1000. − 03	
[←ENG]	1. 00	
[←ENG]	0.001 03	0.001 kilometers

Powers and Roots

Every number has an exponent. If the exponent is not stated, the value is 1. The number to which the exponent refers is called the base. Exponents are printed as a superscript.

Number	Base	Exponent	Same as
x^y	x	y	
$x^{1/y}$	x	$1/y$	$\sqrt[y]{x}$
5^2	5	2	
$5^{1/2}$	5	1/2	$\sqrt{5}$
$5^{3/4}$	5	3/4	$\sqrt[4]{5^3}$

The power key raises the number (or base, x) by multiplying itself by the number of times indicated by the exponent (y).

Calculate $- 32^{29}$

Key in: **Answer:**

32 [+/−] [x^y] 29 [=] $- 4.460149037 \times 10^{43}$

Anything multiplied by itself is called "squared".   The [x^2] key is an operator. How many square yards is a rug that is 11.8 feet on each side?

Key in: **Answer:**

11.8 [x^2] [÷] 9 [=]   **15.47 square yards**

Powers and Roots

A correction needs to be calculated for tape sag when tape is used in surveying. The correction factor is:

$$C = -\frac{W^2 L^3}{24P^2}$$

where: W = tape weight, lb
L = unsupported length of tape, ft
P = Pull on tape, lb

If W = .55, L = 50, and P = 14.2, calculate C:

Key in:	Answer:
.55 $\boxed{x^2}$ $\boxed{\times}$ 50 $\boxed{x^y}$ 3 $\boxed{\div}$ $\boxed{(}$ 24 $\boxed{\times}$ 14.2 $\boxed{x^2}$ $\boxed{=}$ $\boxed{+/-}$	− 7.81 ft.

Root keys are the corollary to power keys. The root is the value which when multiplied by itself y times will equal x. Roots calculated when the values of y are even may be positive or negative. If y is odd, the sign of the root will depend on whether x is positive or negative.

Calculate: $\sqrt{144}$, $\sqrt[5]{-243}$, $\sqrt[0.5]{4}$, and $\sqrt[200]{2 \times 10^{25}}$

Key in:	Answer:
144 $\boxed{x^{1/y}}$ 2 $\boxed{=}$	12
243 $\boxed{+/-}$ $\boxed{x^{1/y}}$ 5 $\boxed{=}$	− 3
4 $\boxed{x^{1/y}}$ .5 $\boxed{=}$	16
2 $\boxed{EXP}$ 25 $\boxed{x^{1/y}}$ 200 $\boxed{=}$	1.33815

A quantity which when multiplied by itself equals the original number is called the square of that number. Square root is a special version of the root key and it is an operator.

Calculate the square root of: 121, .36, .007.

Key in:	Answer:
121 $\boxed{\sqrt{}}$	11
.36 $\boxed{\sqrt{}}$	0.6
.007 $\boxed{\sqrt{}}$	0.08367

Powers and Roots

The radius of curvature (r) for a trapezoidal section is given as:

$$r = \frac{d \sqrt{2 (b_1^2 + 4b_1b_2 + b_2^2)}}{6 (b_1 + b_2)}$$

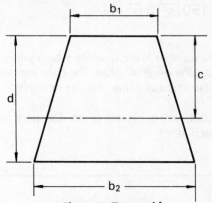

Figure 1: Trapezoid

If $b_1 = 1.2$ feet, $b_2 = 2.5$ feet and d is 5.2 feet, calculate r:

Key in: **Answer:**

1.2 $\boxed{x^2}$ $\boxed{+}$ 4 $\boxed{\times}$ 1.2 $\boxed{\times}$ 2.5 $\boxed{+}$ 2.5 $\boxed{x^2}$ $\boxed{)}$ $\boxed{\times}$
2 $\boxed{)}$ $\boxed{\sqrt{\ }}$ $\boxed{\times}$ 5.2 $\boxed{\div}$ $\boxed{(}$ 6 $\boxed{\times}$ $\boxed{(}$ 1.2 $\boxed{+}$ 2.5 $\boxed{=}$ 1.4699

What is the length of the side of a square which has an area of one acre?
One acre = 43560 square feet.

Key in: **Answer:**

43560 $\boxed{\sqrt{\ }}$ 208.71 ft.

The Talbot formula is used to estimate the size of a culvert for drainage.

$$A = C \sqrt[4]{M^3}$$

where:
C = coefficient based on type of country
M = drainage area, acres

Powers and Roots

If C = 2/3 for rough hill country and M = 150, what pipe size is required?

Key in: ***Answer:***

$$2 \div 3 \times 150 \boxed{x^y} 3 \boxed{x^{\frac{1}{2}}} 4 =$$ **28.57 sq. ft.**

The cube root of a number is the quantity which when multiplied by itself three times equals the original value. The cube root will have only the sign indicated and the original value may be negative.

A building has 3,000,000 cubic feet of interior space and has equalized sides; how big is each side?

Key in: ***Answer:***

$$3 \boxed{\text{EXP}} 6 \boxed{\sqrt[3]{}}$$ **144.22 feet**

Calculate the cube root of − 216:

Key in: ***Answer:***

$$216 \boxed{+/-} \boxed{\sqrt[3]{}}$$ **− 6**

Calculation of water flow in an open channel requires determination of the "critical depth".

$$dc = \sqrt[3]{\frac{Q^2}{b^2 g}}$$

where:
Q = flow, cubic ft/sec
b = channel width, ft
g = gravity 32.2 ft/sec^2

If Q = 1525 cfs and b = 29 feet, what is the critical depth?

Key in: ***Answer:***

$$1525 \boxed{x^2} \div (\ 29 \boxed{x^2} \times 32.2 = \boxed{\sqrt[3]{}}$$ **4.41 feet**

Reciprocal

The reciprocal of a number is one divided by that number. The reciprocal of 4 is 1/4 or 0.25. The reciprocal key is an operator. The reciprocal key helps in calculating fractions when the numerator is 1 and in metric conversions.

Key in:	Answer:
4 $\boxed{1/x}$	**0.25**
$\boxed{1/x}$	**4**

Calculate: 1/50 + 1/20 + 1/4

Key in:	Answer:
50 $\boxed{1/x}$ $\boxed{+}$ 20 $\boxed{1/x}$ $\boxed{+}$ 4 $\boxed{1/x}$ $\boxed{=}$	**0.32**

The conversion from miles to kilometers is 1.6093472. Convert 200 miles to kilometers and that number of kilometers back to miles.

Key in:	Answer:
1.6093472 $\boxed{Min}$	
200 $\boxed{X}$ $\boxed{MR}$ $\boxed{=}$	**321.86944**
$\boxed{X}$ $\boxed{MR}$ $\boxed{1/x}$ $\boxed{=}$	**200**

Factorial

The factorial is important in several areas of mathematics including statistics. The factorial of a number is that number multiplied by itself less one and then by that number less one until one is reached (x is a whole number only).

$$x! = x \times (x-1) \times \ldots \times 4 \times 3 \times 2 \times 1$$
$$5! = 5 \times 4 \times 3 \times 2 \times 1 = 120$$
$$1! = 0! = 1$$

The factorial key is an operator.

Calculate: $10! \div 8!$; $10! - 9!$; $69!$; $70!$

Key in:	Answer:
10 $\boxed{x!}$ $\boxed{\div}$ 8 $\boxed{x!}$ $\boxed{=}$	**90**
10 $\boxed{x!}$ $\boxed{-}$ 9 $\boxed{x!}$ $\boxed{=}$	**3,265,920**
69 $\boxed{x!}$	**$1.711224523 \times 10^{98}$**
70 $\boxed{x!}$	**E**

Note: *The value of the factorial for numbers greater than 69 exceeds the capacity of the calculator and will result in an overflow error.*

Five employees will be evaluated as they work in groups of two. How many different groups are possible?

$$\frac{5!}{(5-2)!} = \frac{5!}{3!}$$

Key in:	Answer:
5 $\boxed{x!}$ $\boxed{\div}$ 3 $\boxed{x!}$ $\boxed{=}$	**20**

The five employees will be drawn from a total of 13 working in a plant. How many combinations of five are possible.

$$\frac{13!}{5! \, (13-5)!} = \frac{13!}{5! \times 8!}$$

Key in:	Answer:
13 $\boxed{x!}$ $\boxed{\div}$ $\boxed{(}$ 5 $\boxed{x!}$ $\boxed{\times}$ 8 $\boxed{x!}$ $\boxed{=}$	**1287**

Factorial

Five women work in the plant; of these groups, how many would include 4 women?

$$\frac{5!}{4! \, (5 \, - \, 4)!} \times \frac{8!}{1! \, (8 \, - \, 1)!} = \frac{5!}{4!} \times \frac{8!}{7!}$$

Key in: ***Answer:***

$$5 \boxed{x!} \boxed{\div} 4 \boxed{x!} \boxed{\times} 8 \boxed{x!} \boxed{\div} 7 \boxed{x!} \boxed{=}$$ **40**

How many groupings will include 5 women?

The above calculation may be carried out directly on calculators that have combination (nCr) and permutation (nPr) keys.

Key in: ***Answer:***

$$13 \boxed{nCr} 5 \boxed{=}$$ **1287**
$$5 \boxed{nCr} 4 \boxed{\times} 8 \boxed{nCr} 1 \boxed{=}$$ **40**

The possible arrangements that can be made from a particular group is called the number of permutations which is defined as:

$$\frac{n!}{(n \, - \, r)!}$$ where:
n = number of objects
r = the number taken at one time

The "Trifecta" in horse racing means selecting and betting on the first, second and third finishers within a race. If there are 8 entrants in a race, what are the odds of winning?

Key in: ***Answer:***

$$8 \boxed{nPr} 3 \boxed{=}$$ **336 (1 out of 336)**

The Trifecta "Box" means selecting the three winners regardless of their order of finish. Selection of a grouping without a specified order is known as a combination. The number of combinations will always be smaller than the number of permutations for the same values.

Key in: ***Answer:***

$$8 \boxed{nCr} 3 \boxed{=}$$ **56**

PART I: Basics

Fractions

The fraction key permits the calculator user to input fractions without converting to decimal. The technique is particularly useful where measurements have been made with a standard type of ruler. The fraction key will also eliminate the use of parenthesis in inverse trigonometric and other scientific calculations.

Calculate: $\quad 1/8 + 3/16 + 3/32 + 5/64; \dfrac{111}{200} + \dfrac{10}{11}$

Note: *The calculator will automatically seek the lowest common denominator. If the denominator exceeds 3 places, the answer will be given in decimal.*

Key in:	**Answer:**
1 $\boxed{a^{b\!/\!c}}$ 8 $\boxed{+}$ 3 $\boxed{a^{b\!/\!c}}$ 16 $\boxed{+}$ 3 $\boxed{a^{b\!/\!c}}$ 32 $\boxed{+}$	
5 $\boxed{a^{b\!/\!c}}$ 64 $\boxed{=}$	**31/64**
$\boxed{a^{b\!/\!c}}$	**0.484375**

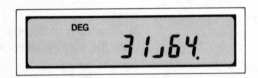

Note: *The answer can be automatically converted to decimal by pressing* $\boxed{a^{b\!/\!c}}$ *again.*

Key in:	**Answer:**
111 $\boxed{a^{b\!/\!c}}$ 200 $\boxed{+}$ 10 $\boxed{a^{b\!/\!c}}$ 11 $\boxed{=}$	**1.4640909**

Fractions

Steel sheets are collected for a construction project. 8 pieces of 00 gage; 6 of gage 2; and 15 of gage 3. What is the total height of the pile of steel?

Note: *U.S. Standard Gage sizes can be found in Table 5.*

Key in: **Answer:**

8 ☒ 11 $a\frac{b}{c}$ 32 ⊞ 6 ☒ 17 $a\frac{b}{c}$ 64 ⊞   8 3/32 inches
15 ☒ 1 $a\frac{b}{c}$ 4 ☰

```
      DEG
    8 3 32.
```

An improper fraction occurs when the numerator is larger than the denominator. The improper fraction can be determined on calculators with a d/c key. In some applications this value may be particularly useful. In the previous example give the answer in 32's.

Key in: **Answer:**

d/c 259/32

```
      DEG
    259 32.
```

Logarithms

Logarithms are a labor-saving device for carrying out complex computations. The use of logarithms reduces multiplication to addition; division to subtraction; raising to a power to multiplication; and extracting a root to division. Much of the need for logarithms has been eliminated by the advent of the pocket calculator.

Nevertheless, these functions are still important because they are included in many mathematical formulations in science and engineering.

The logarithm is defined as the power to which a given base must be raised to produce the given number.

$$L = \log_b N$$

A number can be expressed as a base raised to a power.

$$N = b^L$$

For Instance:

$$b^L = N \qquad L = \log_b N$$

$5^2 = 25$	or	$2 = \log_5 25$
$10^3 = 1000$	or	$3 = \log_{10} 1000$
$10^{-2} = 0.01$	or	$-2 = \log_{10} 0.01$
$3^{1/2} = \sqrt{3}$	or	$1/2 = \log_3 3$

Calculators provide logarithms and the exponential factors for the most common bases: 10 and e as the natural logarithm. The approximate value of e is 2.71828. It is an irrational number resulting from an infinite series.

Logarithms

Base 10 Logarithm, log x

All of the logarithm and antilogarithm keys are operators.

Calculate the logs of: 100,000; 10,000; 1,000; 100; 10; 1; 0.1; 0.01; 0.001; 0.0001; 0.00001

Answers: 5; 4; 3; 2; 1; 0; -1; -2; -3; -4; -5

Noise reduction by the addition of absorbents is computed by the equation:

$$R \text{ (in decibels)} = 10 \log_{10} \frac{Ao + Aa}{Ao}$$

Ao = original
Aa = added

The original surface area (500 sq. feet) of a room is plaster and has a noise reduction coefficient of 0.4. Foam plastic (100 sq. ft. with a 0.9 coefficient) is added to the ceiling. What is the noise reduction?

Key in:	*Answer:*
500 $\boxed{\times}$ .4 $\boxed{+}$ 100 $\boxed{\times}$ .9 $\boxed{)}$ $\boxed{\div}$ $\boxed{(}$	
500 $\boxed{\times}$ .4 $\boxed{=}$ $\boxed{\log}$ $\boxed{\times}$ 10 $\boxed{=}$	**1.6 decibels**

Base e logarithm, ln x

Calculate the natural logs of: 1; 10; 100; 1000

Answers: 0; 2.302585; 4.605170; 6.907755

Base 10 Inverse logarithm or Antilogarithm, 10^x

Calculate the antilogarithms of:

5; 4; 3; 2; 1; 0; -1; -2; -3; -4; -5

Answers:

100,000; 10,000; 1,000; 100; 10; 1; 0.1; 0.01; 0.001; 0.0001; 0.00001

Logarithms

Biological Oxygen Demand (BOD) is the amount of oxygen required for the decomposition of organic material. The difference in oxygen content of a sample at the beginning and end of a given period is the BOD.

$$BOD = (0.2T + 0.6) \; O \; (1 - 10^{-(0.02T + 0.6)K_1 t})$$

where:
T = temperature, °C
O = Oxygen demand at 20°C
K_1 = deoxygenation coefficient at 20°C, 0.1 for sewage

What is the BOD factor, if sewage is stored at 35°C for 20 days?

Key in:	*Answer:*
.02 ⊠ 35 ⊞ .6 ⊜ [Min] ⊠ ⦅ 1 ⊟ ⦅ [MR] [+/−] ⊠ .1 ⊠ 20 ⦆ [10ˣ] ⊜	1.2967

Using logs and antilogs, calculate the value of 5 × 9.

Key in:	*Display:*
5 [log]	0.69897
⊞ 9 [log]	0.9542425
⊜	1.6532125
[10ˣ]	45
5 [ln]	1.6094379
⊞ 9 [ln]	2.1972246
⊜	3.8066625
[eˣ]	45

Physical Constants

Many calculators have physical constants available as direct key ins. The student, scientist, and engineer will find these constants a great help in complex calculations. Use [INV] or [SHIFT] with numbers and operators (shown in parenthesis in examples) to call up physical constants.

Speed of Light in Space (c), [1]

The frequency of a light wave is related to its wavelength by the equation:

$$V = \frac{c}{\lambda} \qquad \text{where:} \quad \lambda = \text{wavelength}$$

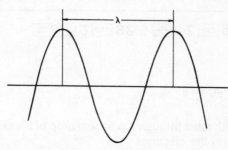

Figure 2: Waves

Note: .0006214 meters to miles conversion.

What is the frequency of an ultraviolet light with a wave length of 10^{-8} meters?

Key in: **Answer:**

[1] [÷] [(] [(] 10 [EXP] 8 [+/−] [X] 6.214 [EXP] 4.82×10^{18} Hz
4 [+/−] [)] [=]

Planck's Constant (h), [2]

The energy carried by a quantum of light (photon energy) according to the physicist Max Planck is:

$E = hv$ where v is the frequency of the light wave

The average frequency of infrared emissions from the earth is 8×10^{13} Hz. Therefore, the photon energy is:

Key in: **Answer:**

8 [EXP] 13 [X] [2] [=] 5.3×10^{-20} Joules

Physical Constants

Gravitational Constant (G), ③

The formula for the acceleration due to gravity of the surface of the earth is:

$$g = \frac{GMe}{Re^2}$$

where:
Me = mass of the earth, 5.9×10^{24}
Re = radius of the earth, 6.38×10^6

Key in: *Answer:*

③ ✕ **5.96** EXP **24** ÷ **6.38** EXP **6** x^2 =   **9.8 m/s²**

Elementary Charge (e), ④

An electron is accelerated through a potential drop of 25000 volts. How much work is done on the electron?

$$W = eV$$

Key in: *Answer:*

2.5 EXP **4** ✕ ④ = 4.01×10^{-15} **Joules**

$$E = mc^2$$

where:
m = mass converted to energy, Kg
c = speed of light
E = equivalent energy in joules

The energy equivalence of one gram of mass is:

Key in: *Answer:*

.001 ✕ ① x^2 = 8.988×10^{13} **Joules**
÷ ④ = 5.6095×10^{32} **eV**

Physical Constants

Electron Rest Mass (Me), 5

Calculate an electron's de Broglie wavelength if it is accelerated to 50 keV. The de Broglie wavelength is:

$$\lambda = \frac{h}{MeV}$$

The equivalent of $MeV = (2Me\ KE)^{1/2}$

Key in:	*Answer:*
2 X 5 X 50000 X 4) √	1.098×10^{-21} **meters**
1/x X 2 =	

Atomic Mass (u), 6

The atomic mass unit is defined as 1/12 of the mass of carbon isotope 12.

The weight of 1 atom of hydrogen is 1674×10^{-24} g. How many grams of hydrogen in 1 gram-atomic weight?

Key in:	*Answer:*
1.674 EXP 24 +/− ÷ (6 X	
1000) =	**1.008090316g**

Note: 6 *must be multiplied by 1000 to convert to grams.*

Calculate the Avogadro Number.

Key in:	*Answer:*
6 X 1000 = 1/x	6.022×10^{23}

Physical Constants

Avogadro Number (Na), ⑦

The atomic weight in grams of a mole of an element is 6.02×10^{23} atoms (the Avogadro Number). Calculate the weight in grams of 1 atomic-weight for hydrogen, helium and oxygen.

Key in:		Answer:
hydrogen	⑦ ÷ ÷ 1.008 =	1.674×10^{-24}
helium	4.003 =	6.647×10^{-24}
oxygen	16 =	26.57×10^{-24}

Boltzmann's Constant (K), ⑧

The Boltzmann Constant is equal to the ideal gas constant divided by the Avogadro Number.

$$K = \frac{R}{N_A}$$

Key in:	Answer:
8.13441 ÷ ⑦ =	1.35×10^{-23} J/K

The kinetic energy of a molecule of ideal gas at 0°C is:

$$KE = 3/2 \ KT$$

Key in:	Answer:
3 ÷ 2 ✕ ⑧ ✕ 273 =	5.65×10^{-21}

Physical Constants

Volume of 1 Kgmole under STP (Vm), ⑨

Under the standard conditions of temperature and pressure (0°C and 760 kgm), a mole of gas occupies .02241383 cubic meters of space. Determine the value of R (general gas law) in liters.

Note: 1 cubic meter = 1000 liters

$$R = \frac{PV}{nT} = \frac{1 \text{ atm} \times 22.4 \text{ liters}}{1 \text{ mole} \times 273° \text{ K}}$$

Key in:	Answer:
⑨ ✕ 1000 ÷ 273 =	0.08210 liter-atm/deg/mole

Electric Constant ϵ_0, ✕

$\epsilon_0 = 8.854 \times 15^{-12}$ Farads/meter and is the permittivity or the dielectric constant (ko) of a vacuum. The capacitance between two plates with a dielectric between the electrodes is:

$$C = KKo \ A/t$$

where:
K = relative dielectric constant
A = Area of the plate
t = distance between the plates

What is the rating of a mica (K = 7.2) capacitor whose electrodes are .1 square meters and separated by 1.5 cm?

Key in:	Answer:
7.2 ✕ ⊠ ✕ .1 ÷ ⦅ 1.5 ÷ 100 =	4.25×10^{-10} Farads

Physical Constants

Magnetic Constant μ_0, ⊞

Permeability measures the ease with which a material's atoms can be aligned to produce magnetic fields. μ_0 is the permeability of air (or vacuum) and is used as the standard against which materials are measured. The reluctance measures the opposition of a material to the "flow" or establishment of magnetic flux.

$$Rm = \frac{l}{\mu_r \mu_0 A}$$

where: l = Length, meters
A = cross section area, meters
μ_r = relative permeability

A .1 meter copper core magnet with a cross section of .13 square meters and μ_r = 0.999998 has what reluctance?

Key in: **Answer:**

.1 ⊟ ⊡ .999998 ⊠ ⊟ ⊠ .13 ⊟   612135.621

Gravity Constant (g), ⊞

g is the rate at which a free falling object accelerates (9.80665 m/s/s). Velocity (speed) equals acceleration times time. What is the speed of an object falling off a tall building after 5 and 15 seconds?

Key in: **Answer:**

⊞ ⊠ ⊠ 5 ⊟   49.03325
15 ⊟   147.09975

Gas Constant (R), ⊟

The ideal gas law states: PV = nRT, where R = 8.31441

An inflated rubber balloon is 2.5 atm. in pressure, 2.8 liters in volume, and 37°C in inside temperature. What is the total number of gas molecules in the balloon?

Key in: **Answer:**

2.5 ⊠ 1.013 EXP 5 ⊠ 2.8 ⊟
⊟ ⊟ ⊡ 273 ⊞ 37 ⊡ ⊠ ⑦ ⊟ $1.656755234 \times 10^{26}$

Angles-Surveying

Establishing positions for construction and determining the location of existing points is the job of the surveyor. From surveying, the need for a clear understanding of the nature of angles is evident.

Any base line may be used to establish directions measured as angles. The line running from north to south is used to reference horizontal direction. An azimuth is an angle measured clockwise from the north while a bearing is a direction expressed as east or west of north or south.

Therefore a 030° azimuth is a bearing of N 30° E and a 240° azimuth S 60° W.

Angle A is an acute angle which is defined as measuring less than a right angle (B). A right angle is two lines perpendicular to each other and an obtuse angle (C) is greater than a right angle.

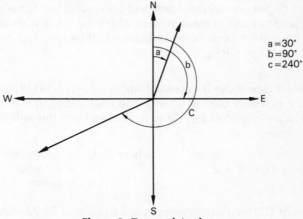

a=30°
b=90°
c=240°

Figure 3: Types of Angles

In both bearings and azimuths the angle is expressed in degrees.

A degree measures the rotation of a line within a circle. The circle is divided into 360 degrees (360°).

Angles-Surveying

The alternative method for measuring an angle uses units called radians. A complete circle consists of 2π radians. The relationships between degrees and radians are:

$$2\pi \text{ radians } = 360° \quad \pi \text{ radians } = 180° \quad 1 \text{ radian } = \frac{180°}{\pi} = 57.2958°$$

Key in: **Answer:**

57.2958 $\boxed{\sqrt{x}}$ 0.0174532

$$1° = \frac{\pi}{180} \text{ radians } = 0.0174532 \text{ radians}$$

Most scientific calculators provide the capability of inputting the value of an angle in degrees or radians. Some will also permit use of the gradient which is a European unit of measurement where the circle is divided into 400 parts. The angular mode of the calculator will be specified in the display as DEG, RAD or GRA.

The symbol π used above is a constant whose value is 3.141592654 (Press to confirm). π is widely used in science and engineering. It is a ratio that relates the circumference of a circle to its diameter and this will hold true for all size circles.

$$C = \pi D = 2\pi R$$

where   C = circumference
        D = diameter
        R = radius

For circles of 100 inch circumference and a radius of 15.92 inches, and C = 3.1415927 meters and R = 1/2 meter, calculate π.

$$\pi = \frac{C}{2R}$$

Key in: **Answer:**

100 $\boxed{\div}$ $\boxed{(}$ 2 $\boxed{\times}$ 15.92 $\boxed{=}$ 3.1407035
3.1415927 $\boxed{\div}$ $\boxed{(}$ 2 $\boxed{\times}$ .5 $\boxed{=}$ 3.1415927

Angles-Surveying

The rectangular coordinate system allows the position of any point in a plane to be defined by two numbers (x, y). The coordinates are formed by perpendicular lines called axes. The two numbers are always stated in the same order. The first number is called the abscissa (x value) and the second, the ordinate (y value)

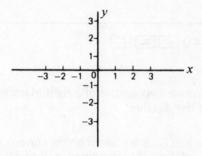

Figure 4: Rectangular Coordinates

Latitude is the term for the distance north or south of the origin. The east or west distance is the departure. The rectangular coordinates divide space into four quadrants. In surveying, most calculations are performed in the first quadrant. Locations are given (latitude, departure).

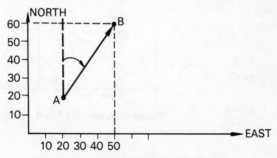

Figure 5: First Quadrant in Surveying

Angles-Surveying

In the figure, point A has coordinates (20, 20) and point B (60, 50). Using the Pythagorean Theorem, the distance AB is:

$$AB^2 = x^2 + y^2 = 30^2 + 40^2$$

Key in: ***Answer:***

30 $\boxed{x^2}$ $\boxed{+}$ **40** $\boxed{x^2}$ $\boxed{=}$ $\boxed{\sqrt{}}$ **50**

The line AB is also the hypotenuse of a right triangle and trigonometry can be used to find the distance.

The trigonometric functions are based on the correspondence of the theoretical relationships of the sides of a right triangle to data obtained by actual measurement. The ratios are based on the concept that two straight lines that make an angle in a drawing or model are the same as the angle in the corresponding structure.

The sine, cosine and tangent of an angle are defined on the basis of the relationships of the sides of a right triangle.

sine $\theta = \dfrac{\text{side A}}{\text{side C}}$

cosine $\theta = \dfrac{\text{side B}}{\text{side C}}$

tangent $\theta = \dfrac{\text{side A}}{\text{side B}}$

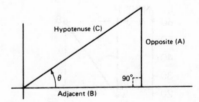

Figure 6: Sides of a Right Triangle

Angles-Surveying

To obtain the value of any trigonometric function on a scientific calculator, place the number in the calculator and then press the function key. Plotting the values of these functions produces the graph pictured in Figure 7.

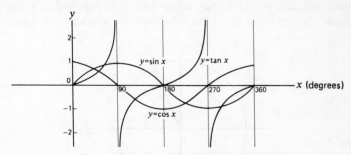

Figure 7: Sine, Cosine, Tangent Functions

Calculate sine of 60°, cosine of 30°, and tangent of 90°.

Note: *Make sure the calculator is in the DEG angular mode, place the value in the calculator and press the proper function key.*

Key in:	*Answer:*
60 sin	**0.8660254**
30 cos	**0.8660254**
90 tan	**Error**

(the tangent of 90° cannot be defined and the calculator so indicates by showing an error sign.)

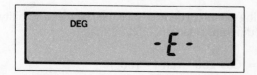

Angles-Surveying

Surveyors and navigators use the North axis to start measuring angles from. The 0° angle is in the North direction and all other angles are measured in a clockwise direction. In trigonometry angles are measured from 0° at the x-axis and counter clockwise. When a circle is imposed on rectangular coordinates in the latter case, the quadrants are as shown in figure 8.

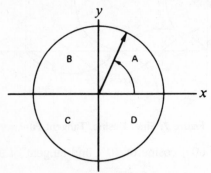

Figure 8: Quadrants

The sign for a trigonometric function as indicated by the quadrant will always be given correctly by the calculator.

If the angle is greater than 360° the calculator will automatically reduce the angle to the equivalent angle less than 360°.

Quadrant	angle range (°)	sine	cosine	tangent
A	0 to 90	+	+	+
B	90 to 180	+	−	−
C	180 to 270	−	−	+
D	270 to 360	−	+	−

The following exercises demonstrate the calculator's ability to handle angles given in different quadrants. Show that:

a. Sin 280° = Cos 260° Tan (− 100°)

b. The identity: $\text{Tan } (A - B) = \dfrac{\text{TanA} - \text{TanB}}{1 + \text{TanA TanB}}$

Angles-Surveying

applies to A = 125°, B = 80° and A = 340°, B = 100°

For 125°, 80°

Key in: **Answer:**

    125 [−] 80 [)] [tan]   **1**

    125 [tan] [−] 80 [tan] [)] [÷]

    [(] 1 [+] 125 [tan] [×] 80 [tan] [=]   **1**

The bearing angle in the surveying example is defined as the angle between the Line AB and the North axis. For the bearing angle:

$$\cos \Delta = \frac{\text{Latitude}}{\text{hypotenuse}} \qquad \sin \Delta = \frac{\text{Departure}}{\text{hypotenuse}}$$

If the angle is given as 36.8699°, what is the value of AB?

Key in: **Answer:**

    40 [÷] 36.8699 [cos] [=]   **50**

    30 [÷] 36.8699 [sin] [=]   **50**

Conversely, coordinates can be computed for a point of known bearing and distance from a point where the coordinates are known.

A 200 foot line is drawn from a point with coordinates (50, 70) and a bearing angle given as π/6. What are the coordinates of the second point?

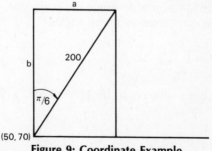

Figure 9: Coordinate Example

Angles-Surveying

Key in:　　　　　　　　　　　　　　　　　　　　　　　　　　　**Answer:**

Mode: RAD

a) $\boxed{\pi}\;\boxed{\div}\;\boxed{6}\;\boxed{)}\;\boxed{\sin}\;\boxed{\times}\;200\;\boxed{=}$　　　　　　**100 feet**

b) $\boxed{\pi}\;\boxed{\div}\;\boxed{6}\;\boxed{)}\;\boxed{\cos}\;\boxed{\times}\;200\;\boxed{=}$　　　　**173.2 feet**

The coordinates are: (223.2, 170).

If the coordinates of a line are known, the bearing angle can be determined by inverse trigonometry. Two lines of a right triangle are the difference in Latitudes ($l_b - l_a$) and the difference in departures ($d_b - d_a$). The bearing angle is the angle with tangent equal to $(d_b - d_a)/(l_b - l_a)$ or Y. It is expressed as:

$\tan^{-1} Y$ or, the angle whose tangent is Y or, the inverse tangent or arc tangent.

The ends of a line are (10, 20) and (40, 60). What is the bearing angle?

$$\frac{40 - 10}{60 - 20} = \frac{30}{40} = 0.75$$

Key in:　　　　　　　　　　　　　　　　　　　　　　　　　　　**Answer:**

.75 $\boxed{\tan^{-1}}$　　　　　　　　　　　　　　　　　　　　　　**36.8699°**

A trigonometric function of an angle has one value. However, with the inverse, the value can represent many angles.

For instance:

$\sin^{-1} 0.5$ is 30° but it also could be 150°, 390°, 510°, etc.

Angles-Surveying

The scientific calculator will always produce the lowest value angle of the inverse function (the "principal value"). The value given by the calculator for an angle resulting from the inverse sine or inverse tangent will always be less than 90° as either a negative or positive quantity; and for inverse cosine it will be between 0° and 180°.

A reading is taken by telescope from 995 feet away of the height of the Washington Monument which is 555 feet. At what angle is the telescope set?

$$\tan C = \frac{A}{B} = \frac{555}{995}$$

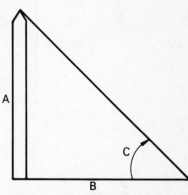

Figure 10: Washington Monument

Key in: **Answer:**

555 [a%] **995** [tan⁻¹]   **29.15°**

Angles-Surveying

A roadway rises 3000 feet over a distance of 1 mile. What is the roadway's grade? Grade is the slope over a horizontal distance of 100 feet.

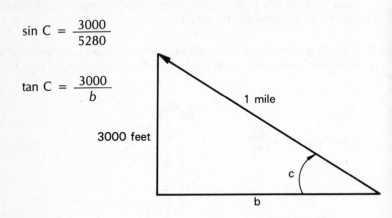

$$\sin C = \frac{3000}{5280}$$

$$\tan C = \frac{3000}{b}$$

3000 feet

1 mile

c

b

Figure 11: Roadway Rise

Key in:	Answer:
300 [a%] 528 [sin⁻¹] [M in]	34.62°
3000 [÷] [MR] [tan] [=]	4344.928 feet
3000 [÷] 43.44928 [=]	69.046 feet/100 feet
	69% Grade

A transit is used to measure horizontal and vertical angles. Readings of the angles are taken on scales called verniers. The sexagesimal technique of angle specification is used.

If the surface of the earth is divided into 360 degrees it can be seen that the area covered by a degree is quite large and a finer technique of measurement is needed. Each degree is further divided into minutes and minutes into seconds. Angles are usually specified in terms of degrees, minutes and seconds rather than their decimal equivalent.

Angles-Surveying

For instance:

40°	30′	32″
degrees	minutes	seconds

To use the trigonometric functions angles must be in their decimal equivalent.

Key in:	**Answer:**

40 ⌊°,,,⌋ 30 ⌊°,,,⌋ 32 ⌊°,,,⌋   **40.508889° decimal**

To calculate the reverse:

Key in:	**Answer:**

⌊←°,,,⌋   **40°30′32″**

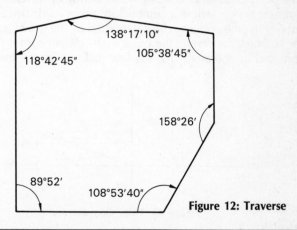

A traverse in surveying is a series of reference points called stations that are connected together. A closed traverse is used in construction to accurately locate building areas. The interior angles of a closed traverse equal (N-2) 180° where N is the number of angles. What is angular error and correction for the traverse in the figure established in the field?

138°17′10″
105°38′45″
118°42′45″
158°26′
89°52′
108°53′40″

Figure 12: Traverse

Angles-Surveying

Add the angles:

Key in: **Answer:**

89 [°'''] **52** [°'''] **[+]**
108 [°'''] **53** [°'''] **40** [°'''] **[+]**
158 [°'''] **26** [°'''] **[+] 105** [°'''] **38** [°'''] **45** [°'''] **[+]**
138 [°'''] **17** [°'''] **10** [°'''] **[+] 118** [°'''] **42** [°'''] **45** [°'''] **[=]**   **719.8388**

[←°'''] **719° 50' 20"**

The required total is 4 × 180 or 720°.

Key in: **Answer:**

720 [−] **719** [°'''] **50** [°'''] **20** [°'''] **[=]**   **0.16111**

Angular error: [←°'''] **0° 9'40"**

Divide by 6 for adjustment to each angle:

Key in: **Answer:**

[°'''] [÷] **6** [=]   **0.02685**

Adjustment: [←°'''] **0° 1' 36.67"**

The new coordinates of a line were previously solved in the rectangular coordinate system where a point is located by its distance from each axis. Alternatively, the point can be determined by the use of polar coordinates. Polar coordinates identify the point by its distance from the center of the system and by the angle that the line makes with the reference axis.

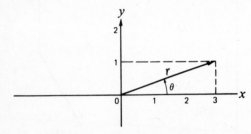

Figure 13: Polar Coordinates

Angles-Surveying

A 200 foot line (same example as figure 9) with bearing angles of a) $\pi/6$ and b) 30° is drawn from point (50, 70). What is the latitude and departure of the second point in each case?

Note: Pressing ⟨x↔y⟩ yields additional data in each case.

Key in:	Answer:
Mode: RAD	
200 ⟨P→R⟩ ⟨ (⟩ ⟨ π ⟩ ⟨ ÷ ⟩ 6 ⟨ = ⟩	173.2
⟨x↔y⟩	100
	(223.2, 170) second point
Mode: DEG	
200 ⟨P→R⟩ 30 ⟨ = ⟩	173.2
⟨x↔y⟩	100

Convert the answers back to length and angle:

Key in:	Answer:
173.2 ⟨R→P⟩ 100 ⟨ = ⟩	199.996 (200)
⟨x↔y⟩	30

Try again using **RAD**.

```
        RAD
0.523611477
```

Note: Multiply the answer 0.523611477 by 6 to verify the value of π.

Hyperbolics

The hyperbolic functions are special combinations of the exponential. These functions are used in many areas of engineering and science.

Hyperbolic sine of $x = \sinh x = \dfrac{1}{2}(e^x - e^{-x})$

Hyperbolic cosine of $x = \cosh x = \dfrac{1}{2}(e^x + e^{-x})$

Hyperbolic tangent of $x = \tanh x = \dfrac{e^x - e^{-x}}{e^x + e^{-x}}$

The inverse hyperbolic functions are:

$\sinh^{-1}x$, $\cosh^{-1}x$, $\tanh^{-1}x$

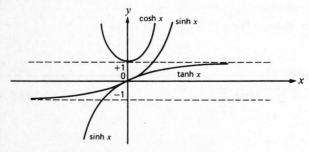

Figure 14: Hyperbolic Functions

Hyperbolics

Calculate the hyperbolic sinh of 100, cosh of 10, and tanh of 6 two ways.

Key in: **Answer:**

a) 100 [hyp] [sin] 1.3440586×10^{43}
b) .5 [×] [( ] 100 [e^x] [−] 100 [+/−] [e^x] [=] 1.3440586×10^{43}

a) 10 [hyp] [cos]   11013.233
b) .5 [×] [( ] 10 [e^x] [+] 10 [+/−] [e^x] [=]   11013.233

a) 6 [hyp] [tan]   0.9999877
b) 6 [e^x] [−] 6 [+/−] [e^x] [ )] [÷] [( ] 6 [e^x] [+]
    6 [+/−] [e^x] [=]   0.9999877

Calculate $\cosh^{-1} 0.5$, $\cosh^{-1} 1.5$, $\sinh^{-1} \pi/4$.

Key in: **Answer:**

.5 [hyp] [cos⁻¹]   E
                                                        (error, see figure 14 for possible
                                                         value of hyperbolic functions.)

1.5 [hyp] [cos⁻¹]   0.9624236
[π] [÷] 4 [ )] [hyp] [sin⁻¹]   0.7212254

Chapter 3 Base Systems and Logic

Bases
ASCII Code
Calculations
Logic Functions

Truth Values
AND, OR
2's Complement

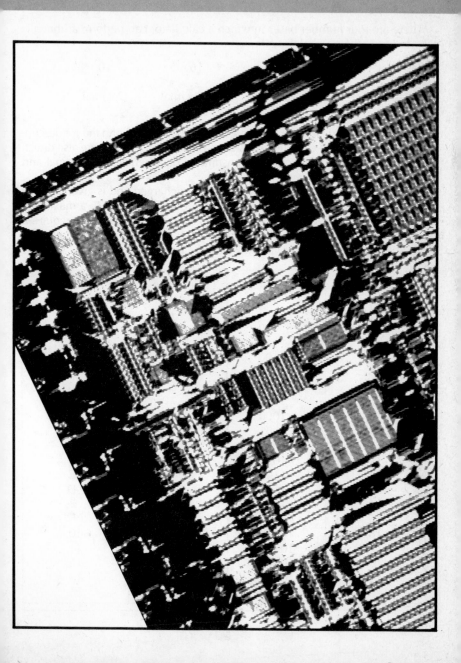

Bases

There are four number bases in which a calculator can perform arithmetic:

Base: 2   8   16   10

Name: Binary   Octal   Hexadecimal   Decimal

Binary, Octal, and Hexadecimal bases provide a useful shorthand for describing the contents of a computer register or a core location. They are also directly related to the ASCII code for transmitting data between a terminal and a computer.

A bit in a computer is either charged or uncharged and is given a value of 0 or 1 (the binary state). To express an octal digit (0 → 7), a maximum of three bits is required. Hexadecimal digits (0 → 9 and A → F) require a maximum of four bits. A 6-bit byte can be described by two octal digits and the more common 8-bit byte by 2 hexadecimal digits.

Decimal	Binary	Octal	Hexadecimal
0	0	0	0
1	1	1	1
2	10	2	2
3	11	3	3
4	100	4	4
5	101	5	5
6	110	6	6
7	111	7	7
8	1000	10	8
9	1001	11	9
10	1010	12	A
11	1011	13	B
12	1100	14	C
13	1101	15	D
14	1110	16	E
15	1111	17	F
16	10000	20	10
17	10001	21	11
18	10010	22	12
19	10011	23	13
20	10100	24	14

PART I: Basics

ASCII Code

Computer information is usually transmitted by ASCII code which is currently described by an eight-bit byte. ASCII gives a standardized value to letters, numbers, and symbols.

Some computer assemblers for the 8080, Z80, 6800, and 6502 cpu's use the octal base to describe ASCII code. The calculator aides in handling problems caused by the octal representation of hexadecimal operations.

ASCII code is not used in calculations. ASCII must first be converted to binary. The decimal digits 0 → 9 are represented in ASCII by:

Base
Decimal	48 → 57
Hexadecimal	30 → 39
Octal	60 → 71

Key in:	**Answer:**
48 [MODE] [3] (HEX)	30
[MODE] [2] (OCT)	60

Computer assembly listings and core dumps are printed in either hexadecimal or octal representation of ASCII code. Each group of hexadecimal or octal digits represent decimal digits, characters, or symbols, or an assembler mnemonic.

Groups of hexadecimal digits are read from left to right in pairs and each pair represents an ASCII character.

ASCII Code

Consider the hexadecimal group 3039.

Key in:	Answer:
[MODE] [3]	
(first pair) 30 [MODE] [0] (DEC)	48
[MODE] [3]	
(second pair) 39 [MODE] [0]	57

With the above procedure ASCII variables may be distinguished from ASCII data.
a) Take the first pair of digits in the hexadecimal group and subtract Hex 30.
b) With a result between 0 and 9 this group is probably data; otherwise it is likely to be a variable.
c) When it is known that the group is data, an ASCII code number greater than 39 will indicate an error.

Calculations

The four arithmetic operations (+, −, ×, ÷) are performed in binary, octal and hexadecimal modes as they are in decimal. Carries and borrows are performed by the calculator within the number base being used.

The fundamental calculation process in both the calculator and computer is done in the binary mode.

Octal and hexadecimal are shorthand for binary. Examples are shown in binary and the equivalent calculations in the three other modes may be done by the reader by switching modes on the calculator.

Calculate: 3 + 2

Key in: *Answer:*

3 [MODE] [1] (BIN)   **Binary 11**
[+] [MODE] [0] 2 [MODE] [1]   **Binary 10**
[=]   **Binary 101**
[MODE] [2]   **Octal 5**
[MODE] [3]   **Hex 5**

Calculate: 2 × 1

Note: *This example demonstrates the properties of multiplication by 2 in decimal, hexadecimal, and octal and the equivalent fundamental computer electronic circuit operation of "shift-left-one-bit" in binary.*

Key in: *Answer:*

1 [MODE] [1]   **Binary 1**
[MODE] [0] 2 [×] [MODE] [1]   **Binary 10**
[MODE] [0] 2 [×]   **Decimal 4**
[MODE] [1]   **Binary 100**

Continue on your own.

Calculations

Each time the number is multiplied by 2, the binary value of 1 (or the bit) is shifted left one place. The process is performed in the computer by an electronic shift register. These circuits along with the logic operations are the fastest in a computer.

The shift function coupled with the logic functions, discussed below, provide a quick means for extracting or inserting a bit or a group of bits anywhere in a computer word.

Calculate: 8 ÷ 2

Note: *This example demonstrates the properties of division by 2 in decimal, hexadecimal, or octal and the fundamental computer electronic circuit of "Shift-right-one-bit" in binary.*

Key in:	Answer:
8 [MODE] [1]	**Binary 1000**
[MODE] [0] [÷] 2 [=]	**Decimal 4**
[MODE] [1]	**Binary 100**
[MODE] [0] [÷] 2 [=]	**Decimal 2**
[MODE] [1]	**Binary 10**

The "divide-by-2" operation simulates the computer's circuit "shift-right-1-bit" and also can be used to extract or insert bits in a computer word.

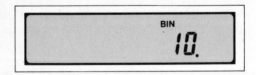

Logic Functions

Function	Logic
AND	A & B false then false or A & B true then true
OR	Either A or B or A & B are true then true
XOR	Either A or B but not A & B are true then true
XNOR	A & B false or A & B true then true
NOT	Forms the 1's complement
NEG	Forms the 2's complement

Logic functions are developed from Boolean algebra. Boole pointed out that if 1 were taken as "true" and 0 as "false", a calculus could be applied to statements that are either true or false (propositional calculus). True or false statements can be applied to switching theory in the design of electronic circuits and computers.

These functions can be illustrated by electric light circuits:

AND

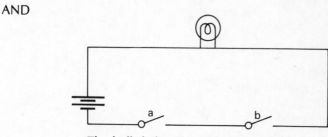

The bulb lights if a and b are closed.

OR (inclusive) Circuit

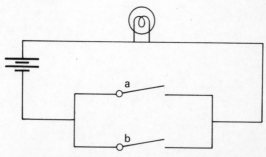

The bulb lights if a or b or both are closed.

Logic Functions

XOR (exclusive) Circuit

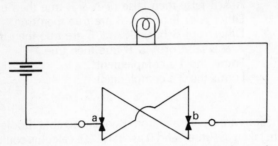

The bulb lights if a or b, but not both, is closed.

Note: *The diagram shows both a and b in the off position.*

Truth Values

The Boolean truth values 0 and 1, correspond to the preceding circuits as follows:

AND

AND	A	
	0	1
B $\{$ 0	0	0
1	0	1

OR (Inclusive)

OR	A	
	0	1
B $\{$ 0	0	1
1	1	1

XOR (Exclusive)

XOR	A	
	0	1
B $\{$ 0	0	1
1	1	0

NOR

NOR	A	
	0	1
B $\{$ 0	1	0
1	0	0

NOT	I	
	0	1
	1	0

Logic functions operate "bit-wise" (vertically). There is no carry or borrow as in arithmetic functions.

AND, OR

Let A = 3 and B = 5:

Key in: ***Answer:***

[MODE] [3] 5 [X↔M]
         3 [X↔M]
[MODE] [1]   **Binary 101**
              [X↔M]   **Binary 11 (Hex 3)**

[AND] [MR] [=] Compares Bin 101 with Bin 11   **Binary 1**

The binary bits have been logically
AND'ed together in corresponding
pairs.

[X↔M] Binary 101 still in memory
[AC]
11 [OR] [MR] [=] Compares Bin 101 with Bin 11   **Binary 111**

The binary bits have been logically OR'ed together in corresponding pairs.

In the computer language, BASIC, three Boolean functions are used: AND, OR, and NOT. These Boolean operators combine conditions on a bit-by-bit basis. For example, consider the following BASIC statement:

20 PRINT X OR Y

Preceded by:

10 Let X = 3: Let Y = 5

Running this program will yield an answer of 7. In Binary bits: 011 OR 101 = 111. Each bit in one operator is OR'ed with the corresponding bit in the other. Simulate this program on your calculator.
Change Line 20 to:

20 PRINT X AND Y

PART I: Basics

AND, OR

Running the program will now yield 1. In Binary bits: 011 AND 101 = 001. Each bit is AND'ed with the corresponding bit.

For IF statements in BASIC the terms "true" and "false" must be related to the IF conditions. The term "true" relates to IF statements as anything but zero and the THEN part of the statement is executed if the condition equals anything except zero. "False" relates to IF statements as zero. For example:

10 IF J > 0 OR K = 1 THEN PRINT "YES"

The condition J > 0 is evaluated and yields either 1 or 0. The condition K = 0 is evaluated and yields either 1 or 0. These two conditions are OR'ed together. If the result is other than zero then "YES" is printed. Otherwise, the IF statement is finished and the computer program continues to the next statement.

Arithmetic with Logic Functions

Key in:	Answer:
[MODE] [1] **1111 [X] 10** (decimal 2) [=]	**11110**

All bits shifted left one position

Masking

If the fifth bit in the above result is not wanted, i.e., the carry into the fifth bit must be removed, use the procedure:

Key in:		Answer:
[MODE] [1] **1111** [Min]		
[X] **10** [=] [AND] [MR] [=]	Shifts the bit pattern 1 digit left Strips off the carry bit and maintains the integrity of the 4-bit half-byte	**1110**

2's Complement

2's complement arithmetic takes the place of subtraction on many computers. The 2's complement of a number is taken to form a negative.

Calculate: 5 − 3

Key in:		*Answer:*
5		
MODE 1 Min	Stores Binary 101 in memory	
MODE 0 3 MODE 1		**Binary 11**
NOT	All the bits are complemented	1111111100
+ 1 =	Forms the 2's complement	1111111101
+ MR =	Adds Bin 101 to value displayed	**Binary 10**
MODE 0		**Decimal 2**
or: MODE 1 **101** Min		
11 ENG + MR =		**Binary 10**

Calculate − 14 in hexadecimal.
1) 14 − 1 is 13
2) 13 in binary is 1101
3) NOT 13 is 0010
4) binary 0010 in HEX is 2
5) The negative number − 14 is represented by FFFFFFF2
6) 14 in HEX is E. Therefore, E plus FFFFFFF2 should be 0. Try it.

Statistical Analysis

A manufacturer of dot matrix computer printers tests 10 of each 500 units produced for failure rate. The sample is chosen by generating random numbers between 0 and 500.

Note: *Change the mode to* **FIX 0** *so that answers will be whole numbers. Your answers should, of course, be different.*

Key in:	Answer:
[RAN#] [X] 500 [=]	405
[RAN#] [X] 500 [=]	289
(Repeat 8 more times)	

The 10 printers, randomly selected out of the 500, are run until they fail. Failure (measured in millions of lines) occurs at: 5.2, 4.8, 4.6, 4.6, 5.8, 6.1, 5.3, 5.3, 5.3, and 4.4.

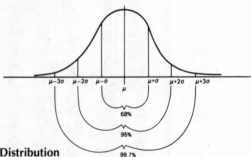

Figure 15: Normal Distribution

The significance of such data can be analyzed by statistical techniques based on the theory of normal distribution (central tendency.) A normal distribution describes the distribution of many physical phenomena and will form the familiar bell-shaped curve. The area under a normal curve represents the entire "population" (all data). The population must have a large number of elements. Sample estimates of the parameters are not meaningful statistically unless the number of samples is 10 or more. The mode is the axis of symmetry of the normal curve. The frequency of data near the mode will be greatest and the distribution of data will form the bell shape.

The average or mean of a normal distribution is μ and on the calculator is $\bar{x}$. The average is defined as:

$$\bar{x} = \frac{x_1 + x_2 + x_3 + \cdots x_n}{n} \quad \text{where } n = \text{number of samples}$$

Statistical Analysis

Key in:

Mode: SD   SAC
      5.2 XD (or X)
      4.8 XD
   4.6×2 XD
      5.8 XD
      6.1 XD
   5.3×3 XD
      4.4 XD

NOTE: XD *is the data entry key. Data may be placed into the calculator with a "weight" as in two of the above entries.*

Press n to check the number of entries (in this case, 10).

Key in:	*Answer:*
$\bar{x}$	5.14

Check by getting the total of the x's (Σx) and dividing by the number of samples.

Key in:	*Answer:*
Σx ÷ n =	5.14

Small sigma (σ) represents the standard deviation which is the measure of dispersion of data from the mean. The more the data is dispersed, the higher will be the value of σ relative to the mean. σ_n is the standard devia-

Statistical Analysis

tion for the entire population and σ_{n-1} is for the sample. The sample will always be higher than the population σ because of the uncertainty inherent in the sample. The formula for the deviations are:

$$\sigma_n = \sqrt{\frac{\Sigma x^2 - n\bar{x}^2}{n}} \qquad \sigma_{n-1} = \sqrt{\frac{\Sigma x^2 - n\bar{x}^2}{n-1}}$$

The values for 68% of the population will fall within one standard deviation and 95% within 2 and 99.7% within 3.

Calculate the range of values for one and 2 standard deviations in the example.

Key in:	Answer:
$\boxed{\bar{x}}\ \boxed{+}\ \boxed{\sigma_{n\text{-}1}}\ \boxed{=}$	**5.686**
$\boxed{\bar{x}}\ \boxed{-}\ \boxed{\sigma_{n\text{-}1}}\ \boxed{=}$	**4.594**

68.2% of the failures will occur between 4.594 and 5.686

$\boxed{\bar{x}}\ \boxed{+}\ 2\ \boxed{\times}\ \boxed{\sigma_{n\text{-}1}}\ \boxed{=}$	**6.232**
$\boxed{\bar{x}}\ \boxed{-}\ 2\ \boxed{\times}\ \boxed{\sigma_{n\text{-}1}}\ \boxed{=}$	**4.048**

95.45% between 4.048 and 6.232

Change the last data to 3.9. Calculate the number of standard deviations that will include all of the samples.

Note: *Parenthesis do not work in the statistics mode.*

Key in:	Answer:
$4.4\ \boxed{\text{DEL}}\ 3.9\ \boxed{x\text{D}}$	
Lowest Value $\ 3.9\ \boxed{-}\ \boxed{\bar{x}}\ \boxed{=}\ \boxed{\div}\ \boxed{\sigma_{n\text{-}1}}\ \boxed{=}$	**−1.8688**
	(−2 Standard Deviation)
Highest Value $\ 6.1\ \boxed{-}\ \boxed{\bar{x}}\ \boxed{=}\ \boxed{\div}\ \boxed{\sigma_{n\text{-}1}}\ \boxed{=}$	**1.586**
	(+2 Standard Deviation)

If a decimal occurs in the results of this type of analysis, always round up to determine the number of standard deviations.

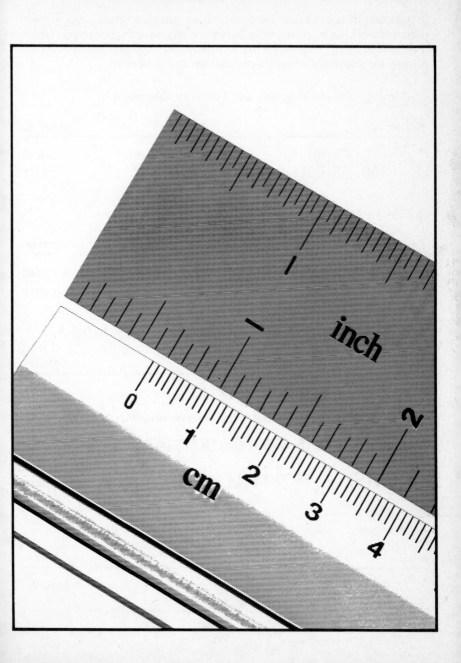

Conversion Keys

Calculators with built-in conversion have two directional keys ◄ ►. One of these keys is pressed to indicate the direction of the conversion where the number to be converted is in the display. The displayed number is converted automatically when the conversion key is pressed.

1. Convert 32°F to centigrade and 100°C to Fahrenheit.

Key in:	Answer:
32 ► °F⇄°C	**0°C**
100 ◄ °F⇄°C	**212°F**

2. Convert 100 mm to inches and 10 inches to millimeters.

Key in:	Answer:
100 ► in⇄mm	**2540**
10 ◄ in⇄mm	**0.3937**

3. If gasoline costs $1.15 per gallon, what is the cost of 10 liters?

Key in:	Display	Answer:
1.15 ◄ gal⇄ℓ .303798 ✕ 10 =		**$3.04**

$15.00 buys 60 liters. What is the per gallon cost?

60 ◄ gal⇄ℓ 15.85033 1/x ✕ 15 =		**$0.95/gallon**
or: **15 ► gal⇄ℓ 56.78115 ÷ 60 =**		**$0.95/gallon**

4. How many pounds in a kilogram?

Key in:	Answer:
1 ◄ lb⇄kg	**2.2046 lb.**

Conversion Keys

5. Sixteen ounces equals how many grams?

Key in: **Answer:**

    16 `▶` `oz⇋g`   **453.592**

6. The amount of heat (energy transferred) required to raise a gram of water from 14.5°C to 15.5°C is called a calorie. Joule showed that mechanical work could be converted into heat. 4.184 joules of energy is the accepted value of 1 calorie. Convert 100 calories to joules and 100 joules to calories.

Key in: **Answer:**

    100 `▶` `cal⇋J`   **418.605 J**
    100 `◀` `cal⇋J`   **23.89 C.**

7. The atmosphere at sea level has a pressure of 14.7 pounds per square inch. Mercury is used to measure pressure in a guage. One atmosphere is equal to 760 mm Hg and 1.0129×10^5 pascal. Pascal developed the principle that pressure on a fluid at rest is distributed equally and the pressure from that fluid is dependent on the height of the column of that fluid. Pressure is a force acting perpendicular to a surface within a unit area. Change 760 mm Hg to KPa.

Key in: **Answer:**

    760 `▶` `mmHg⇋kPa`   **101.32472 KPa**

8. An atmosphere of pressure equals 100,000 Pascals.
   Convert an atmosphere to mPa.

Key in: **Answer:**

    `1` `▶` `atm⇋MPa`   **0.101325**

Chapter 1 **Math**

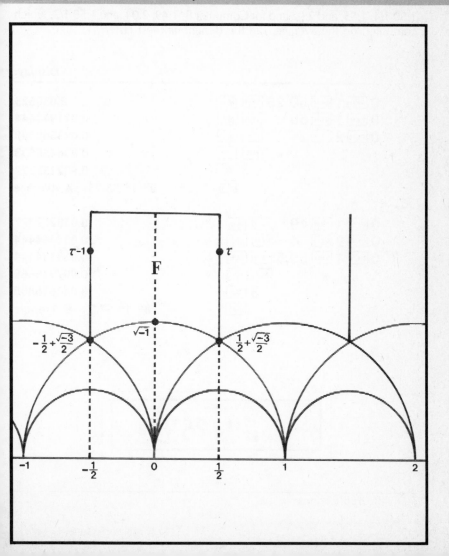

Time Conversions

Benchmark tests are used to check a computer's computational speed and accuracy. The test is a computer program that usually generates a table of numbers. The same program is used on each computer.

Analyzing the results of these tests, the actual times can be converted to their decimal equivalents by using the same calculator keys that are used to convert an angle given in minutes and seconds.

The Benchmark program is run on the Pear IIe (A) and the Banana Model III (B), three times in each case. If the times recorded for Computer A are 1:50 1/4, 1:55, and 2:02 and for Computer B: 1:49, 2:04, and 1:59 1/2, which computer, on the average, ran the Benchmark test faster?

Key in:	Display:
0 [°'"] 1 [°'"] 50.25 [°'"] [Min]	0.030625
0 [°'"] 1 [°'"] 55 [°'"] [M+]	0.031944444
0 [°'"] 2 [°'"] 2 [°'"] [M+]	0.033888888
[MR] [÷]	0.096458333
3 [=]	0.032152777
[°'"]	0° 1° 55.75 *A Average*
0 [°'"] 1 [°'"] 49 [°'"] [Min]	0.030277777
0 [°'"] 2 [°'"] 4 [°'"] [M+]	0.034444444
0 [°'"] 1 [°'"] 59.5 [°'"] [M+]	0.033194444
[MR] [÷]	0.097916666
3 [=]	0.032638888
[°'"]	0° 1° 57.5 *B Average*

A is faster.

$$0°1°57.5$$

Time Conversions

A computer systems analyst visits a client from 12:15 P.M. to 4:56 P.M. How many hours may the analyst charge?

Key in: **Answer:**

4 [o:••] 56 [o:••] [−] 0 [o:••] 15 [o:••] [=]   **4.6833 hours**

[o:••]   **4 hours 41 minutes**

Note: *If the time period extends beyond noon or midnight, add 12 to the later time.*

Calculate the hours from 7:45 A.M. to 6:05 P.M.

Key in: **Answer:**

18 [o:••] 5 [o:••] [−] 7 [o:••] 45 [o:••] [=]   **10.333 hours**

[o:••]   **10 hours 20 minutes**

```
  10°20°0.
```

Triangle Problems

The law of sines and law of cosines are ratios derived from the trigonometric functions that can be used to solve all triangles.

The law of sines results from the observation that the sides of a triangle are proportional to the sines of the angles they subtend.

The law of sines states:

$$\frac{a}{\text{Sin}A} = \frac{b}{\text{Sin}B} = \frac{c}{\text{Sin}C}$$

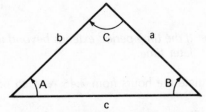

Figure 16: Generalized Triangle

The law of cosines states:

$$a^2 = b^2 + c^2 - 2bc \text{ Cos } A$$

The cosine of 90° is 0. The law of cosines for a right triangle reduces to $a^2 = b^2 + c^2$, the Pythagorean Theorem.

Triangle Problems Generalized

Type	Given	Solved by
I	1 side, 2 angles	law of sines
II	2 sides, angle opposite them	law of sines
III	2 sides, included angle	law of cosines
IV	3 sides	law of cosines adjusted to:

$$\cos A = \frac{b^2 + c^2 - a^2}{2bc}$$

Triangle Problems

Examples:

Type I: A plane sights 2 ships sailing at a distance of 500 feet apart. The angles of depression to each ship are 5° and 15°. How high in a vertical plane is the plane?

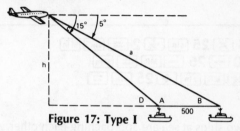

Figure 17: Type I

Note 1: *The angles B and D correspond to the angles of depression. Angle C is 15° minus 5°, or 10°. Angle A is 180° — D, or 165°. Using the law of sines solve for value a. h will be a function of the sine of B.*

$$\frac{a}{\sin 165°} = \frac{500}{\sin 10°} \quad \sin 5° = \frac{h}{a} \text{ (by completing the rectangle)}$$

Key in: **Answer:**

Step 1: **165** [sin] [×] **500** [÷] **10** [sin] [=] [Min]   a = 745.24 feet
Step 2: **5** [sin] [×] [MR] [=]   h = 64.95 feet

Type II: The distance between two buoys is two miles. It is known that the distance to Buoy B from a point on shore is 1.5 miles. How far is it to Buoy A?

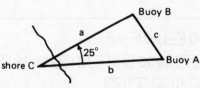

Figure 18: Type II

Triangle Problems

$$\frac{a}{\sin A} = \frac{c}{\sin 25°} \quad B = 180 - C - A \quad \frac{b}{\sin B} = \frac{c}{\sin 25°}$$

$$\sin A = a \sin 25°/c \quad b = c \sin B/\sin 25°$$

Key in:	**Answer:**
Step 1: **1.5** [X] **25** [sin] [÷] **2** [=] [sin⁻¹] [Min]	18.48°
Step 2: **180** [−] **25** [−] [MR] [=] [Min]	136.52°
Step 3: **2** [X] [MR] [sin] [÷] **25** [sin] [=]	3.26 miles

Type III: Two ships at sea are approaching each other. A lighthouse keep-
er observes that one ship is 6829 feet away and the other 8900
feet away and they subtend an angle of 110°50′2″. How far apart
are the two ships using the law of cosines?

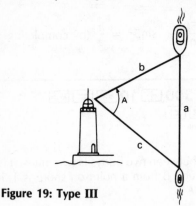

Figure 19: Type III

Key in: **Answer:**

110 [°′″] **50** [°′″] **20** [°′″] [Min]

6829 [x²] [+] **8900** [x²] [−] **2** [X] **6829** [X]

8900 [X] [MR] [cos] [)] [√]   13,003.377 feet

Triangle Problems

Type IV: A sail measures 10′ × 12′ × 8′. How many square yards of sail cloth are required?

Note: *Use the law of cosines, adjusted, to find Angle A.*

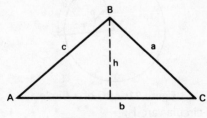

Figure 20: Type IV

The area of a triangle is:
  K = 1/2hb. h is equal to c sinA:
  K = 1/2cb sinA
  Divide by 9 to convert square feet to square yards.

$$\cos A = \frac{8^2 + 12^2 - 10^2}{2 \times 8 \times 12}$$

Key in: **Answer:**

8 $\boxed{x^2}$ $\boxed{+}$ 12 $\boxed{x^2}$ $\boxed{-}$ 10 $\boxed{x^2}$ $\boxed{)}$ $\boxed{\div}$ $\boxed{(}$ 2 $\boxed{\times}$
8 $\boxed{\times}$ 12 $\boxed{=}$ $\boxed{\cos^{-1}}$
.5 $\boxed{\times}$ 12 $\boxed{\times}$ 8 $\boxed{\times}$ 55.77 $\boxed{\sin}$ $\boxed{=}$
39.68 $\boxed{\div}$ 9 $\boxed{=}$ 4.4089 sq. yards

Navigation

Take a sphere. Intersect it through the center with a plane and a great circle is produced. An arc on a great circle is measured by the angle it subtends. A spherical triangle is made up of three arcs of great circles.

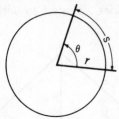

Figure 21: ARC of a Circle

The length of a circular arc is:

S = $r\theta$, where r = radius

A common unit of measurement at sea is the nautical mile. The nautical mile is defined as: the arc length subtended on a circle of diameter 7917.59 miles (earth) by a central angle of 1' (one minute). How long is a nautical mile?

$$r = \frac{1}{2} (7917.59) (5280) \text{ and } \theta = \frac{1}{60} \times \frac{\pi}{180}$$

$$s = \frac{1}{2} (7917.59) (5280) \frac{\pi}{60 \times 180}$$

Key in: ***Answer:***

.5 ⊠ 7917.59 ⊠ 5280 ⊠ π ÷ ((

60 ⊠ 180 ⊜   6,080.27 feet

To convert miles to nautical miles:

Key in: ***Answer:***

5280 ÷ 6080.27 ⊜   0.86838

A knot is a measure of the speed of a ship based on the nautical mile. It is equivalent to nautical miles/hour.

Two points on the same meridian are 18° north of the equator and 6° 30' south of the equator. What is the distance between the two points?

Use the arc formula s = $r\theta$

r is the radius of the earth. θ is the angle in radians.

Navigation

Converting to radians:

the angle $\times \dfrac{\pi}{180}$

$$s = \frac{1}{2}(7915.6) \times \overset{\text{angle}}{(18 + 6.5)}\left(\frac{\pi}{180}\right)$$

Key in: **Answer:**

.5 ☒ 7915.6 ☒ ⟮ ⟮ ⟮ 18 ⊞ 6.5 ⟯ ☒

⟮ ⟮ π ⟯ ÷ 180 ⊜   **1,692.38 miles**

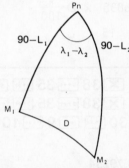

Figure 22: Spherical Triangle

A ship steaming at 15 knots sails the great-circle route from New York to Lisbon. How long will the trip take? New York is latitude = 40°40′N and longitude = 73°58′30′′W and Lisbon is L = 38°35′N and = 9°10′W.

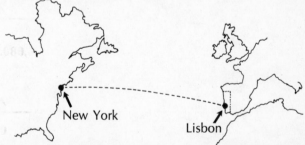

New York

Lisbon

Note: *Great-circle navigation is based on the spherical triangle.*

The standard formula for determining the distance between 2 locations (M_1, M_2) is $\cos D = \sin L_1 \times \sin L_2 + \cos L_1 \times \cos L_2 \times \cos DL_0$, where:

$$DL_0 = \lambda_1 - \lambda_2$$
$$M_1 = L_1, \lambda_1 \qquad M_2 = L_2, \lambda_2$$

(South Latitude and East Longitude are entered as negative)

PART II: Applications

Navigation

The answer D will be in terms of the angle of the arc. To convert to miles use the arc formula. Divide the answer by knots to get the time.

$$\text{Cos } D = \sin 40°40' \times \sin 38°35' + \cos 40°40' \times \\ \cos 38°35' \times \cos (73°58'30'' - 9°10')$$

$$S = \frac{1}{2} \overset{\substack{nautical \\ conversion}}{(7915.6 \times 0.86838)} \times D \frac{\pi}{180}$$

Time = S ÷ Knots = S ÷ 15

Key in: **Answer:**

40 [°'''] 40 [°'''] [sin] [×] 38 [°'''] 35 [°'''] [sin] [+]
40 [°'''] 40 [°'''] [cos] [×] 38 [°'''] 35 [°'''] [cos] [×]
[(] 73 [°'''] 58 [°'''] 30 [°'''] [−] 9 [°'''] 10 [°'''] [)] [cos] [=]

                                                                                        0.6587874

[cos⁻¹] [Min]   **D = 48.79254**
.5 [×] 7915.6 [×] 0.86838 [×] [MR]
[×] [(] [π] [÷] 180 [=]   **2,926.81 nautical miles**

[÷] 15 [=]   **195.12 hours**

Parabola Length

The formula for determining the length of an arc(s) of a parabola is:

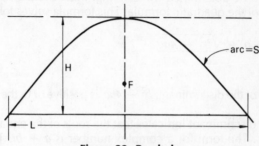

Figure 23: Parabola

$$S = 2L \left[\sqrt{N^2 + \frac{1}{16}} + \frac{1}{16N} \left(LN \left(N + \sqrt{N^2 + \frac{1}{16}} \right) + LN4 \right) \right]$$

where $N = \dfrac{H}{L}$

If H is 20 feet and L is 90 feet, what is the length of S?

Key in: ***Answer:***

20 ÷ 90 = Min
x^2 + 1 a%⁄ 16) √ + (((1 ÷ (16 ×
MR))) × (((MR + ((MR x^2 + 1 a%⁄ 16)
√)) ln + 4 ln))))) × 2 × 90 =

100.7376 feet

Quadratic Equations

$ax^2 + bx + c = 0$ is the form of the quadratic equation. The roots (values of x) can often be determined by factoring. Most situations, however, require the use of the quadratic formula. This formula solves for x as follows:

$$x = \frac{-b \pm \sqrt{b^2 - 4ac}}{2a}$$

If the value of the discriminant, $b^2 - 4ac$, is positive or 0, the roots are real.

A negative discriminant indicates that the roots of the equation are complex numbers. The form for a complex number is $a + bi$. The quadratic formula is divided into two parts. The second part has an i added to it, indicating that the discriminant has been multiplied by $\sqrt{-1}$.

Calculate the roots of:

a. $4x^2 + 18x - 8$
b. $2x^2 + 4x + 2$
c. $10x^2 + 22x + 1000$
d. $.1x^2 + .01x + .001$

Key in:	*Answer:*
a) 18 $\boxed{x^2}$ $\boxed{-}$ 4 $\boxed{\times}$ 4 $\boxed{\times}$ 8 $\boxed{+\!/\!-}$ $\boxed{=}$	**452 discriminant**
$\boxed{\sqrt{\ }}$ $\boxed{\text{Min}}$	
18 $\boxed{+\!/\!-}$ $\boxed{+}$ $\boxed{\text{MR}}$ $\boxed{)}$ $\boxed{\div}$ $\boxed{(}$ 2 $\boxed{\times}$ 4 $\boxed{=}$	**0.40754 Root 1**
18 $\boxed{+\!/\!-}$ $\boxed{-}$ $\boxed{\text{MR}}$ $\boxed{)}$ $\boxed{\div}$ 8 $\boxed{=}$	**− 4.908 Root 2**
b) 4 $\boxed{x^2}$ $\boxed{-}$ 4 $\boxed{\times}$ 2 $\boxed{\times}$ 2 $\boxed{=}$	**0 discriminant**
4 $\boxed{+\!/\!-}$ $\boxed{\div}$ 4 $\boxed{=}$	**− 1 Root**
c) 22 $\boxed{x^2}$ $\boxed{-}$ 4 $\boxed{\times}$ 10 $\boxed{\times}$ 1000 $\boxed{=}$	**− 39516**
22 $\boxed{+\!/\!-}$ $\boxed{\div}$ 20 $\boxed{=}$	**− 1.1 (a)**
39516 $\boxed{\sqrt{\ }}$ $\boxed{\div}$ $\boxed{(}$ 2 $\boxed{\times}$ 10 $\boxed{=}$	**9.939 (b)**
	− 1.1 ± 9.939 i
d) .01 $\boxed{x^2}$ $\boxed{-}$ 4 $\boxed{\times}$ .1 $\boxed{\times}$ .001 $\boxed{=}$	**− 3 × 10⁻⁴**
.01 $\boxed{+\!/\!-}$ $\boxed{\div}$ .2 $\boxed{=}$	**− 0.05 (a)**
3 $\boxed{\text{EXP}}$ 4 $\boxed{+\!/\!-}$ $\boxed{\div}$ .2 $\boxed{=}$	**0.0015 (b)**
	− 0.05 ± .0015 i

PART II: Applications

Polynomials

A polynomial is one type of mathematical statement. The number of parts of the equation is determined by the value of n which is also a superscript.

$$p(x) = a_n x^n + \ldots + a_2 x^2 + a_1 x + a_0$$

Evaluate the following equation for $x = -10$, 10 and 100

$$p(x) = 6x^4 + 2x^3 - 14x^2 + 50$$

Key in:	Answer:
10 [+/-] [Min]	
6 [×] [MR] [x^y] 4 [+] 2 [×] [MR] [x^y] 3	
[−] 14 [×] [MR] [x^2] [+] 50 [=]	**56650**
for 10	**60650**
for 100	**601860050**

$$\text{M} \quad 601860050.$$

Series

A mathematical series is a statement with an infinite number of terms. There is no way to calculate every term in a particular series. The value of a function described as a series is therefore an approximation. The greater the number of terms evaluated in the series, the greater will be the accuracy of the approximation.

A definite integral is:

$$\int_0^x \sin y^2 dy = \frac{x^3}{3} - \frac{x^7}{7(3!)} + \frac{x^{11}}{11(5!)} - \frac{x^{15}}{15(7!)}$$

Find the values of the integral for $x = 1, .5,$ and $.1$.

Note: *The intermediate results in the display show how with each additional term, the result becomes more consistent.*

Key in:	**Display:**

For $x = 1$:

1 $a\%$ 3 $-$ 1 $a\%$ 7 $\div$ 3 $x!$ $+$	**13/42**
1 $a\%$ 11 $\div$ 5 $x!$ $-$	0.310281385
1 $a\%$ 15 $\div$ 7 $x!$ $=$	0.310268157

For $x = .5$:

.5 x^y 3 $\div$ 3 $-$	0.041666666
.5 x^y 7 $\div$ $($ 7 $\times$ 3 $x!$ $)$ $+$	0.041480654
.5 x^y 11 $\div$ $($ 11 $\times$ 5 $x!$ $)$ $-$	0.041481024
.5 x^y 15 $\div$ $($ 15 $\times$ 7 $x!$ $)$ $=$	0.041481024

For $x = .1$:

.1 x^y 3 $\div$ 3 $-$	3.333333333 -04
.1 x^y 7 $\div$ $($ 7 $\times$ 3 $x!$ $)$ $+$	3.333309524 -04
.1 x^y 11 $\div$ $($ 11 $\times$ 5 $x!$ $)$ $=$	3.333309524 -04

Another definite integral is:

$$\int_0^x e^{-y^2} dy = x - \frac{x^3}{3} + \frac{x^5}{5(2!)} - \frac{x^7}{7(3!)} + \ldots..$$

Note: *Use as many items as necessary to stabilize the answer.*

Series

Calculate for $x = 1, .5,$ and .1.

Key in:	Display:
For 1: 1 $\boxed{-}$ 1 $\boxed{a\%}$ 3 $\boxed{+}$	2/3
1 $\boxed{a\%}$ 10 $\boxed{-}$	23/30
1 $\boxed{a\%}$ 7 $\boxed{\div}$ 3 $\boxed{x!}$ $\boxed{+}$	26/35
1 $\boxed{a\%}$ 9 $\boxed{\div}$ 4 $\boxed{x!}$ $\boxed{-}$	0.7474867
1 $\boxed{a\%}$ 11 $\boxed{\div}$ 5 $\boxed{x!}$ $\boxed{+}$	0.7467292
1 $\boxed{a\%}$ 13 $\boxed{\div}$ 6 $\boxed{x!}$ $\boxed{=}$	0.746836
For .5: .5 $\boxed{-}$ .5 $\boxed{x^y}$ 3 $\boxed{\div}$ 3 $\boxed{+}$	0.4583333
.5 $\boxed{x^y}$ 5 $\boxed{\div}$ 10 $\boxed{-}$	0.4614583
.5 $\boxed{x^y}$ 7 $\boxed{\div}$ 42 $\boxed{=}$	0.4612723
For .1: .1 $\boxed{-}$ .1 $\boxed{x^y}$ 3 $\boxed{\div}$ 3 $\boxed{+}$	0.099666666
.1 $\boxed{x^y}$ 5 $\boxed{\div}$ 10 $\boxed{-}$	0.099667666
.1 $\boxed{x^y}$ 7 $\boxed{\div}$ 42 $\boxed{=}$	0.099667664

Length of An Ellipse

The length of an ellipse is a series:

$$L = \pi(a+b)\left[\ 1+\frac{1}{4}\left(\frac{a-b}{a+b}\right)^2 + \frac{1}{64}\left(\frac{a-b}{a+b}\right)^4 + \frac{1}{256}\left(\frac{a-b}{a+b}\right)^6 + ...\right]$$

Calculate: for $a = 50$ and $b = 10$

Key in: **Answer:**

50 $\boxed{-}$ 10 $\boxed{)}$ $\boxed{\div}$ $\boxed{(}$ 50 $\boxed{+}$ 10 $\boxed{=}$ $\boxed{x^2}$ $\boxed{Min}$ 1 $\boxed{+}$
$\boxed{MR}$ $\boxed{\div}$ 4 $\boxed{+}$ $\boxed{MR}$ $\boxed{x^2}$ $\boxed{\div}$ 64 $\boxed{+}$ $\boxed{MR}$ $\boxed{x^y}$ 3 $\boxed{\div}$
256 $\boxed{=}$ $\boxed{\times}$ $\boxed{(}$ 50 $\boxed{+}$ 10 $\boxed{)}$ $\boxed{\times}$ $\boxed{\pi}$ $\boxed{=}$

210.08593 feet

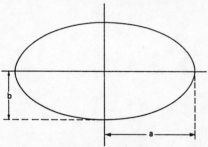

Figure 24: Ellipse

Simpson's Rule

The value of a definite integral may be approximated by Simpson's Rule. The curve defining the integral with vertical lines at the beginning point (a) and ending point (b) to the x-axis creates an area which is the value of the integral. The area is divided into an even number of parts (n). The greater the number of parts, the more exact is the approximation. Each part is defined as $(b$-$a) \div n$.

The total area is:

$$\int_a^b f(x)\ dx = \frac{\Delta x}{3}\ (f_0\ +\ 4f_1\ +\ 2f_2\ +\ 4f_3\ +\ 2f_4\ +\ ...\ +\ 4f_{n-1}\ +\ f_n)$$

> f_0 is $f(x)$ with $x = a$
> f_1 is $f(x)$ with $x = a + \Delta x$
> f_2 is $f(x)$ with $x = a + 2\Delta x$
> f_n is $f(x)$ with $x = b$

If $b = 6$, $a = 3$, and $n = 6$, calculate the total value of the definite integral:

$$f(x) = 2x^3 + 2.85x^2 - 6.8$$

Key in: **Answer:**

6 ⊟ 3 ⟀ ⊞ 6 🟰   .5

Simpson's Rule

Part	Key in:									Answer:

Part   **Key in:**   **Answer:**

f_0 2 ⊠ 3 x^y 3 ⊞ 2.85 ⊠ 3 x^2 ⊟ 6.8 ⊟ Min

$4f_1$ 2 ⊠ 3.5 x^y 3 ⊞ 2.85 ⊠ 3.5 x^2 ⊟ 6.8 ⎵
⊠ 4 M+

$2f_2$ 2 ⊠ 4 x^y 3 ⊞ 2.85 ⊠ 4 x^2 ⊟ 6.8 ⎵
⊠ 2 M+

$4f_3$ 2 ⊠ 4.5 x^y 3 ⊞ 2.85 ⊠ 4.5 x^2 ⊟ 6.8 ⎵
⊠ 4 M+

$2f_4$ 2 ⊠ 5 x^y 3 ⊞ 2.85 ⊠ 5 x^2 ⊟ 6.8 ⎵
⊠ 2 M+

$4f_5$ 2 ⊠ 5.5 x^y 3 ⊞ 2.85 ⊠ 5.5 x^2 ⊟ 6.8 ⎵
⊠ 4 M+

f_n 2 ⊠ 6 x^y 3 ⊞ 2.85 ⊠ 6 x^2 ⊟ 6.8 M+

MR ⊠ .5 ⎵ ÷ 3 ⊟   **766.65**

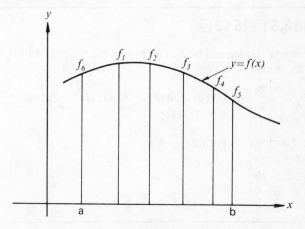

Figure 25: Simpson's Rule

Matrices

A matrix is a table of related numbers in a rectangular shape. The convention followed is that the horizontal lines are called rows and the verticals are called columns. A number in a matrix is identified as (row #, column #).

Multiply each element in the following matrix by 3.5.

$$A = \begin{bmatrix} 324 & 410 & 422 \\ 489 & 117 & 695 \end{bmatrix}$$

Note: *Use the calculator's constant feature. K appears on the display.*

Key in:	**Answer:**
3.5 $\boxed{\times}$ $\boxed{\times}$ 324 $\boxed{=}$	**1134**
489 $\boxed{=}$	**1711.5**
410 $\boxed{=}$	**1435**

etc.

$$A^1 = \begin{bmatrix} 1134 & 1435 & 1477 \\ 1711.5 & 409.5 & 2432.5 \end{bmatrix}$$

Add 512 to (1,2) in A^1.

Note: *The first row and the first column in a matrix are designated as 0.*

Key in:	**Answer:**
2432.5 $\boxed{+}$ **512** $\boxed{=}$	**2944.5**

A square matrix is a special type of matrix. In many applications, its "determinant" must be calculated.

$$d \begin{vmatrix} x_1 & y_1 & z_1 \\ x_2 & y_2 & z_2 \\ x_3 & y_3 & z_3 \end{vmatrix} = x_1 y_2 z_3 + x_2 y_3 z_1 + x_3 y_1 z_2 - x_1 y_3 z_2 - x_3 y_2 z_1 - x_2 y_1 z_3$$

Calculate the determinant for:

$$\begin{vmatrix} 1 & 4 & 7 \\ 2 & 5 & 8 \\ 3 & 6 & 9 \end{vmatrix}$$

Key in:	**Answer:**
5 $\boxed{\times}$ 9 $\boxed{+}$ 2 $\boxed{\times}$ 6 $\boxed{\times}$ 7 $\boxed{+}$ 3 $\boxed{\times}$ 4 $\boxed{\times}$ 8 $\boxed{-}$	
6 $\boxed{\times}$ 8 $\boxed{-}$ 3 $\boxed{\times}$ 5 $\boxed{\times}$ 7 $\boxed{-}$ 2 $\boxed{\times}$ 4 $\boxed{\times}$ 8 $\boxed{=}$	**8**

Chapter 2 **Statistics**

Linear Regression
"t" Test
Chi-Square Test

Linear Regression

The development of a relationship between two sets of data with x and y values is called regression. When the relationship is a straight line, the relationship is called "linear regression". The equation for the line is:

$y = a + bx$

where b = slope, a = y axis crossing point of the line.

The correlation (r) is a measure of the reliability of the relationship between the x and y values. The best value for r is 1. Values of r close to 1 represent excellent reliability. If the correlation coefficient is relatively far from 1, the predictions based on the relationship will be less reliable. The equation for the correlation coefficient is:

$$r = \frac{n\Sigma(xy) - \Sigma(x)\Sigma(y)}{\sqrt{[n\Sigma x^2 - (\Sigma x)^2] \times [n\Sigma y^2 - (\Sigma y)^2]}}$$

The thickness of a layer of silver deposited on an integrated circuit chip is a function of time spent in a vacuum evaporator. The experimental data is:

Minutes in Furnace	Average Thickness (mils)
1	.0132
1.5	.0151
2.0	.0167
2.5	.0177
3.0	.0211

Check the correlation and predict the thickness at 2.2 minutes. How long would a thickness of .016 take?

A. Using a calculator with 2-variable statistics:

Key in:

Mode: LR   KAC

1	x_D, y_D	.0132 DATA
1.5	x_D, y_D	.0151 DATA
2	x_D, y_D	.0167 DATA
2.5	x_D, y_D	.0177 DATA
3	x_D, y_D	.0211 DATA

Linear Regression

Once data has been placed into the calculator, the correlation coefficient (r), the constant (a), and the slope (b) are obtained:

Key in: **Answer:**

$\boxed{r}$	.9814
$\boxed{\text{A}}$	9.4×10^{-03}
$\boxed{\text{B}}$	3.68×10^{-03}

Estimates of other values on the correlation line are:

Key in: **Answer:**

2.2 $\boxed{\hat{y}}$	.0175 mils (estimated y)
.016 $\boxed{\hat{x}}$	1.793 minutes (estimated x)

B. Using a calculator with one-variable statistics

Note: *Use the statistics mode to determine the values for x and y.*

Key in: **Answer:**

Mode: SD $\boxed{\text{SAC}}$
  1 $\boxed{xD}$ 1.5 $\boxed{xD}$ 2 $\boxed{xD}$ 2.5 $\boxed{xD}$ 3 $\boxed{xD}$ $\boxed{\Sigma x^2}$ 22.5
                                                                    $\boxed{\Sigma x}$ 10
  $\boxed{\text{SAC}}$ .0132 $\boxed{xD}$ .0151 $\boxed{xD}$ .0167 $\boxed{xD}$
  .0177 $\boxed{xD}$ .0211 $\boxed{xD}$ $\boxed{\Sigma x^2}$ 1.43964×10^{-3}
                                                                    $\boxed{\Sigma x}$ .0838

  $\boxed{\text{M+}}$ $\boxed{\text{MODE}}$ $\boxed{0}$

Note: *Calculate $\Sigma\ (XY)$.*

Linear Regression

Key in:	Answer:

.0132 ⊞ 1.5 ⊠ .0151 ⊞ 2 ⊠ .0167 ⊞
2.5 ⊠ .0177 ⊞ 3 ⊠ .0211 ⊟   .1768

$\overset{n}{5}$ ⊠ $\overset{\Sigma(xy)}{.1768}$ ⊟ $\overset{\Sigma x}{10}$ ⊠ $\overset{\Sigma y}{\text{MR}}$ ⊡ ⊟ ⊂ ⊂ ⊂

$\overset{n}{5}$ ⊠ $\overset{\Sigma x^2}{22.5}$ ⊟ $\overset{\Sigma(x^2)}{100}$ ⊃ ⊠ ⊂ $\overset{n}{5}$ ⊠ $\overset{\Sigma y^2}{1.43964}$

EXP 3 ⊬ ⊟ MR $\overset{\Sigma y}{x^2}$ ⊃ ⊃ ⊃ √ ⊟   .9814

$$B = \frac{n\Sigma xy - \Sigma x\Sigma y}{n\Sigma x^2 - (\Sigma x)^2} \qquad A = \frac{\Sigma y - B\Sigma x}{n}$$

Key in:	Answer:

5 ⊠ .1768 ⊟ 10 ⊠ .0838 ⊃
⊡ ⊂ 5 ⊠ 22.5 ⊟ 100 ⊟ X↔M 3.68×10^{-03} (B)
.0838 ⊟ MR ⊠ 10 ⊃ ⊡ 5 ⊟ 9.4×10^{-3} (A)

Therefore, the straight line equation is:

$y = .0094 + .00368 \times$

To estimate other values on the correlation line:

Key in:	Answer:

.0094 ⊞ .00368 ⊠ 2.2 ⊟   .0175 mils
.016 ⊟ .0094 ⊃ ⊡ .00368 ⊟   1.793 minutes

"t" Test

In the earlier discussion of printer failure (page 72) a small sample was used (less than 30 is a "small" sample in statistics). The hypothesis used can be checked with the "t" test. The t-distribution is close to the normal distribution.

$$t = \frac{\bar{x} - \mu_0}{\sigma_{n-1}/\sqrt{n}}$$

where: $\bar{x}$ = sample mean
σ_{n-1} = sample standard deviation
n = sample size
μ_0 = required population mean

A buyer of computer printers requires a mean life of 4.9 million lines. If these printers are purchased, will the buyer be safe within a 5% level of confidence?

From the "statistics" section:

$n = 10$ $\bar{x} = 5.14$ $\sigma_{n-1} = 0.546$

Key in: **Answer:**

5.14 ⊟ 4.9 ⊐ ÷ ⊏ .546 ÷ 10 √ =   **1.39**

The value for t at 5% confidence level with a sample size of 10 is 1.83 (see the "t" values table in the appendix). The calculated t is 1.39 (less than 1.83) and the buyer can conclude the printers being purchased are probably from a population with a mean failure rate equal to or greater than 4.9 million lines 95% of the time.

Chi-Square Test

Experience over a number of years with a test given to computer service technicians at the end of a training course indicates that 60% of the trainees will score between 70 and 80 (C); 20% between 81 and 90 (B); 5% 91 or more (A) and 15%, 69 or less (D). In a recent class of 200, the marks were:

Group	A	B	C	D
Number	9	33	100	58

Is the difference between the marks on this particular exam and the expected distribution of marks based on history due to chance?

The data is analyzed by the X^2 test. The test is generally used to determine if a set of data when compared to an idealized distribution has a variance from probability or a preset expectation greater than would have been expected by chance.

$$X^2 = \sum \frac{(O - E)^2}{E}$$

where: O = Observed frequency
E = Expected frequency

Frequency of Test Scores

Grade Level	%	Expected # (% × 200)	Actual #
A	5	10	9
B	20	40	33
C	60	120	100
D	15	30	58

Key in: *Answer:*

$9 \boxed{-} 10 \boxed{)} \boxed{x^2} \boxed{\div} 10 \boxed{+} \boxed{(} 33 \boxed{-} 40 \boxed{)} \boxed{x^2}$
$\boxed{\div} 40 \boxed{+} \boxed{(} 100 \boxed{-} 120 \boxed{)} \boxed{x^2} \boxed{\div} 120 \boxed{+}$
$\boxed{(} 58 \boxed{-} 30 \boxed{)} \boxed{x^2} \boxed{\div} 30 \boxed{=}$ **30.792**

The *df* (degrees of freedom) for this problem is 3. The $X^2_{0.05}$ column in the chi-square values table in the appendix is the line which divides 5% of the right tail of the distribution from the remainder of the distribution. The degrees of freedom were determined by taking one less than the number of sample proportions being tested.

The $X^2_{0.05}$ for this problem is 7.82. The value obtained by the test, 30.792, is substantially higher. The results indicate that the difference between what was expected to be scored in the tests and what was actually happening in this case was due to factors other than chance.

Chapter 3 **Physics**

Projectiles

A projectile shot or launched into space has two components to its motion, horizontal and vertical. The horizontal velocity (x-direction) remains constant while the vertical is affected by gravity as a function of time (free falling body).

$$Vx = Vo \cos\theta \quad Vy = Voy - gt$$

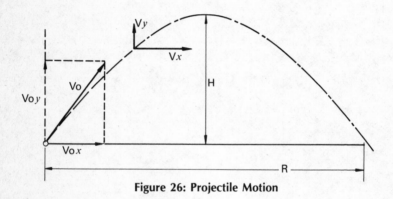

Figure 26: Projectile Motion

The resultant velocity at any point on the trajectory is:

$$V = \sqrt{Vx^2 + Vy^2}$$

At the top of a trajectory $Vy = 0$ and the time of flight to that point is:

$$t - \frac{Voy}{g} = \frac{Vo \sin\theta}{g}$$

The range (R) is:

$$R = Vox\,(2T) = \frac{2Vo^2\cos\theta \sin\theta}{g}$$

Projectiles

The identity $\sin 2\theta = 2 \cos \theta \sin \theta$ is substituted to get:

$$R = \frac{Vo^2}{g} \sin 2\theta$$

The height is:

$$H = \frac{Vo^2 \sin^2\theta}{2g}$$

If a bullet is shot at a velocity of 1,500 feet per second, at what angle will maximum range be obtained? What is the maximum height at this angle and how long will the bullet be in flight?

Key in:	Answer:
velocity [FIX] [1] 1500 [x^2] [÷] 32.2 [=] [Min]	
for 10°: 20 [sin] [×] [MR] [=]	23898.9 feet
for 30°: 60 [sin] [×] [MR] [=]	60514.2 feet
for 45°: 90 [sin] [×] [MR] [=]	69875.8 feet
for 60°: 120 [sin] [×] [MR] [=]	60514.2 feet
for 85°: 170 [sin] [×] [MR] [=]	12133.8 feet

The answer is 45°.

for H:

Key in:	Answer:
[MR] [÷] 2 [×] 45 [sin] [x^2] [=]	17468.9 feet

for *t:*

Key in:	Answer:
1500 [×] 45 [sin] [÷] 32.2 [=]	32.9 seconds

Orbitting

The speed at which an orbiting object travels is a function of distance and mass. The equation applies to an electron in an atom as well as a planet circling the sun.

$$V = \sqrt{2GM\left(\frac{1}{r} - \frac{1}{2a}\right)}$$

where: r = radius at a given point on the orbit.
a = mean distance from the central object.
M = mass of the central object
G = universal grivitional constant 6.668 $\times$ 10^{-23}.

If at a point in its orbit the earth is 92 million miles from the sun, what is its speed at this radius and at the mean distance? The mass of the sun is 1.992 $\times$ 10^{33}kg, and the mean distance is 92.96 $\times$ 10^6miles.

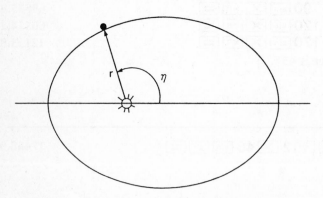

Figure 27: Sun at Focus of Ellipse of Planet in Drbit

Orbitting

Key in: **Answer:**

Convert miles to kilometers.

92 [EXP] 6 [×] 1.60935 [=] 148.06 [EXP] 6 [=]
92.96 [EXP] 6 [×] 1.60935 [=] [Min] 149.605 [EXP] 6 [=]
148.06 [EXP] 6 [1/x] [−] [(] [(] 2 [×] [MR] [)] [1/x] [)] [×] 2 [×]
6.668 [EXP] 23 [+/−] [×] 1.992 [EXP] 33 [=] [√]

30.1 kilometers/second

[MR] [1/x] [−] [(] [(] 2 [×] [MR] [)] [1/x] [)] [×] 2 [×] 6.668
[EXP] 23 [+/−] [×] 1.992 [EXP] 33 [=] [√] **29.8 kilometers/second**

An elliptical orbit is measured by its eccentricity. A higher eccentricity indicates an elliptical path that is more elongated. The eccentricity of orbit of the earth is 0.0161718. What is the polar angle at $r = 92$ million miles?

$$\eta = \cos^{-1}\left[\ \frac{1}{e} - \frac{a(1 - e^2)}{re}\ \right]$$

Key in: **Answer:**

Mode: RAD

.016718 [1/x] [−] [(] [(] [(] 92.96 [×] [(] 1 [−]
.016718 [x²] [)] [)] [)] [÷] [(] 92 [×] .016718 [=]
[cos⁻¹]   **2.2234 radians**

[×] 180 [÷] [π] [=]   **127.39°**

Radioactive Decay

The radioactive substance radium-226 decays by the emission of a helium atom (alpha particle) to radon-222:

$$_{88}Ra^{226} \longrightarrow {}_{86}Rn^{222} + {}_{2}He^{4}$$

weights (amu)

226.01544   222.01761   4.00260

Calculate the mass difference and the energy released (ΔMc^2)

Key in: **Answer:**

226.02544 ⊟ 222.01761 ⊟ 4.00260 ⊜

5.23×10^{-3} amu mass difference

⊠ ⑥ ⊜ 8.68476×10^{-30} kg mass difference

⊠ ① x^2 ⊜ 7.8055×10^{-13} Joules Energy Released

⊟ ④ ⊜   4871771.69 eV Energy Released

ENG ENG   4.87 MeV Energy Released

$$\boxed{0.004871753 \quad {}^{09}}$$

Viscosity

Viscosity is the force exerted by layers of fluid passing over each other. Measurement is in poise (η), or centipoise, named after the Frenchman Poiseuille. One poise equals 1 dyne-sec/cm^2. The Poiseuille equation relates flow volume to viscosity, pressure drops and the physical characteristics of the pipe.

$$Q = \frac{(P_2 - P_1)\pi R^4}{8L\eta}$$

where: P = pressure
R = pipe radius
L = pipe length

Acetone (η = 0.337 cp) flows through 200 feet of a .5-inch pipe in a factory with a pressure drop of 100 psi (pounds/square inch). What is the flow volume?

To convert Dynes/cm^2 to psi multiply by 1.45038 × 10^{-5}.

Key in: **Answer:**

100 ☒ π ☒ .5 x^y 4 ÷ 〔 8 ☒ 200 ☒
12 ☒ .337 EXP 2 ⁺∕₋ ☒ 1.45038 EXP 5 ⁺∕₋ ☰

20922.7 in^3/sec

÷ 1728 ☰   12.1 ft^3/second

What pressure drop must be overcome when SAE 30 oil (η = 60 cp) flows at a rate of 400 cubic inches/second through 30 feet of 1-inch i.d. pipe?

Solving for the pressure drop:

$$P = \frac{8QL\eta}{\pi R^4}$$

Key in: **Answer:**

8 ☒ 400 ☒ 30 ☒ 12 ☒ 60 EXP 2 ⁺∕₋ ☒
1.45038 EXP 5 ⁺∕₋ ÷ π ☰   3.191 psi

Gas Laws

The combining of Boyle's Law with Charles' Law results in the General Gas Law:

$$\frac{P_1 V_1}{T_1} = \frac{P_2 V_2}{T_2}$$

Charles' Law is:

$$\frac{V_1}{T_1} = \frac{V_2}{T_2}$$

where: V = volume
T = absolute temperature °C + 273

The volume of gas is proportional to the temperature. The higher the temperature, the greater the volume if pressure is constant.

500 ml of a gas is heated from 10°C to 30°C. What is the volume at the higher temperature?

$$V_2 = \frac{V_1 T_2}{T_1}$$

Key in: **Answer:**

500 ⊠ 〔 30 ⊞ 273 〕 ÷ 〔
10 ⊞ 273 ⊜   **535.34 ml**

The volume of a fixed mass of gas at constant temperature is inversely proportional to the pressure. If pressure goes up, volume goes down. The value of pressure times volume becomes a constant.

$$P_1 V_1 = P_2 V_2$$

What pressure is required to reduce 200 ml of a gas at 75 psi to 50 ml?

$$P_2 = \frac{P_1 V_1}{V_2}$$

Gas Laws

Key in: **Answer:**

200 ✕ 75 ÷ 50 =   **300 psi**

If a gas fills a 50-litre cube at 10°C, 2 atmospheres, what pressure will it be at if it is moved to a 75-litre cube at 20°C?

$$P_2 = \frac{P_1V_1T_2}{T_1V_2}$$

Key in: **Answer:**

2 ✕ 50 ✕ 283) ÷ (293 ✕ 75 =   **1.288 atm.**

The ideal gas equation equates the pressure, volume and temperature of a particular gas to the number (n) of molecules of that gas. The equation is balanced by use of the ideal gas constant R which equals 0.0821 litre-atm/mole°K. The equation is written:

$$PV = nRT$$

What is the volume of 5 moles of nitrogen at 10°C and a pressure of 500 mm Hg? To convert to atmospheres, multiply mm Hg by .001315.

$$V = \frac{nRT}{P}$$

Key in: **Answer:**

5 ✕ .0821 ✕ 283) ÷ (500 ✕
.001315 =   **176.69 liters**

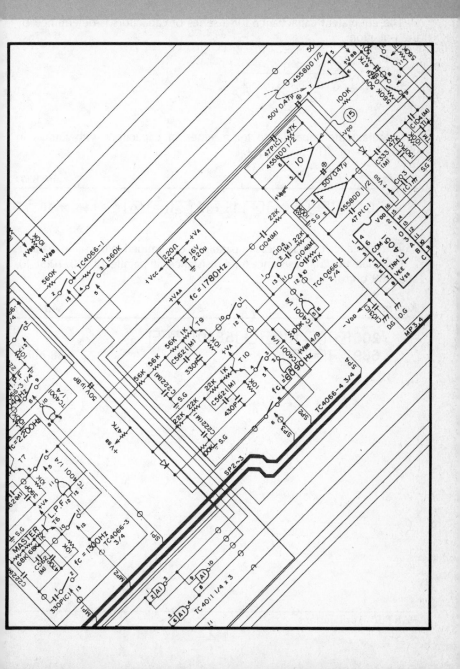

Series Capacitance & Parallel Resistance

The equivalent capacitance for a series of capacitors is determined by the equation:

$$C = \cfrac{1}{\cfrac{1}{C_1} + \cfrac{1}{C_2} + \cfrac{1}{C_3} \cdots \cfrac{1}{C_n}}$$

Calculate the capacitance for a series of capacitors with ratings in microfarads of .01, .5, 1 and 2.

Key in: **Answer:**

.01 $\boxed{1/x}$ $\boxed{+}$ .5 $\boxed{1/x}$ $\boxed{+}$ 1 $\boxed{+}$ 2 $\boxed{1/x}$ $\boxed{=}$ $\boxed{1/x}$ **$9.66 \times 10^{-3} \mu F$**

The resistance of resistances in parallel is determined in the same manner.
Calculate the total resistance for 4 resistances in parallel of 200, 10,5840, and 689 ohms.

Key in: **Answer:**

---

200 $\boxed{1/x}$ $\boxed{+}$ 10 $\boxed{1/x}$ $\boxed{+}$ 5840 $\boxed{1/x}$ $\boxed{+}$
689 $\boxed{1/x}$ $\boxed{=}$ $\boxed{1/x}$ **9.38 ohms**

Circuits with Alternating Current

In alternating current circuits, the concept of impedance replaces resistance in the relationship between the applied voltage and current flow. Each circuit will have resistors, inductors, and capacitance. The voltage (electromotive force) flows in a sinusoidal pattern. The phase angle is a measurement of the degree to which the current and voltage are out of phase with each other due to inductive reactance or capacitive reactance.

In a series circuit:

$$Z = R^2 + \left(\omega L - \frac{1}{\omega C} \right)^2 \qquad \text{Impedance magnitude } \omega = 2\pi f$$

$$\theta = \tan^{-1} \left(\frac{\omega L - \frac{1}{\omega C}}{R} \right) \qquad \text{Impedance phase angle}$$

where: R = Resistance
       L = Inductance
      C = Capacitance
     ω = Angular frequency
     f = frequency

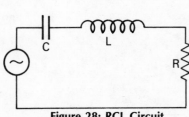

Figure 28: RCL Circuit

Calculate the impedance and phase angle for a circuit where f = 60 Hz, L = 5 mH, C = 9μF, and R = 6240 ohms.

Key in:	*Answer:*

2 $\boxed{\times}$ $\boxed{\pi}$ $\boxed{\times}$ 60 $\boxed{=}$ $\boxed{\text{Min}}$
$\boxed{\times}$ 5 $\boxed{\text{EXP}}$ 3 $\boxed{+/-}$ $\boxed{-}$ 1 $\boxed{\div}$ $\boxed{(}$ $\boxed{\text{MR}}$ $\boxed{\times}$ 9 $\boxed{\text{EXP}}$ 6 $\boxed{+/-}$
$\boxed{=}$ $\boxed{\text{Min}}$ $\boxed{x^2}$ $\boxed{+}$ 6240 $\boxed{x^2}$ $\boxed{)}$ $\boxed{\sqrt{\ }}$ **6246.87 ohms**

$\boxed{\text{MR}}$ $\boxed{\div}$ 6240 $\boxed{=}$ $\boxed{\tan^{-1}}$ **− 2.69°**

Circuits with Alternating Current

The impedance equations change when the resistance, capacitance and inductance are in parallel to:

$$Z = \frac{1}{\sqrt{\frac{1}{R^2} + \left(\frac{1}{\omega L} - \omega C\right)^2}} \qquad \theta = \tan^{-1} R\left(\frac{1}{\omega L} - \omega C\right)$$

Calculate for the same values as above:

Key in:	**Answer:**
2 $\boxed{\times}$ $\boxed{\pi}$ $\boxed{\times}$ 60 $\boxed{=}$ $\boxed{\text{Min}}$ $\boxed{\times}$ 5 $\boxed{\text{EXP}}$ 3 $\boxed{+/-}$ $\boxed{)}$ $\boxed{1/x}$ $\boxed{-}$ $\boxed{\text{MR}}$ $\boxed{\times}$ 9 $\boxed{\text{EXP}}$ 6 $\boxed{+/-}$ $\boxed{=}$ $\boxed{\text{Min}}$ $\boxed{x^2}$ $\boxed{+}$ 6240 $\boxed{x^2}$ $\boxed{1/x}$ $\boxed{)}$ $\boxed{\sqrt{}}$ $\boxed{1/x}$	1.897 ohms
$\boxed{\text{MR}}$ $\boxed{\times}$ 6240 $\boxed{=}$ $\boxed{\tan^{-1}}$	89.98°

$$\boxed{89.9825809}$$

R-C Time Constants

Circuits containing capacitance and resistance have a time constant which is a resultant of the two (TC = RXC). The five factors are the Voltage (E), Vc (Voltage across the capacitor) (V), resistance (R), capacitance (C), and time (T). Any one of these can be computed if the other four are known. The input limits are:

    10,000 > R > 0.000999 kohms
    10,000 > C > 0.000999 mfds
    10,000 > E > 0.000999 volts
    10,000 > T > 0.000999 msec
    10,000 > VC > 0.000999 volts

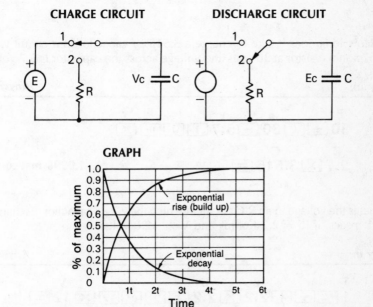

Figure 29: R-C Circuit

R-C Time Constants

Charge Formulas

$$R = \frac{T}{C \times Ln\,(E/E-V)}$$

$$T = R \times C \times Ln\,(E/E-V)$$

$$E = \frac{V}{1 - e^{(-T/RC)}}$$

$$V_R = E - V$$

$$I = \frac{VR}{R}$$

Discharge Formulas

$$R = \frac{T}{C \times Ln\,(E/V)}$$

$$T = R \times C \times Ln\,(E/V)$$

$$E = \frac{V}{e^{(-T/RC)}}$$

$$V_R = E - V$$

$$I = \frac{VR}{R}$$

How long does it take to charge a 3.515 μf capacitor in a circuit with a 2.7 kohm resistor at 30 volts and voltage across the capacitor is 5.7 volts?

Key in: **Answer:**

$$\overset{E}{30} \div \big(\; \overset{E}{30} - \overset{V}{5.7}\;\big)\big)\; \boxed{\text{ln}}\; \boxed{\times}$$

$$\overset{R}{2.7} \boxed{\times} \overset{C}{3.515} \boxed{=}$$
                                     1.9998 mseconds

What is the voltage in an R-C circuit in which the 2.2 μf capacitor discharges in 1 msecs, if R = 2.2 Kohms and V = 12.0 volts?

Key in: **Answer:**

$$\overset{T}{1} \boxed{+/-} \div \big(\; \overset{R}{2.2} \boxed{\times} \overset{C}{2.2}\;\big)\big)\; \boxed{e^x}\; \boxed{1/x}\; \boxed{\times}\; \overset{V}{12}\; \boxed{=}$$
                                     14.754 volts

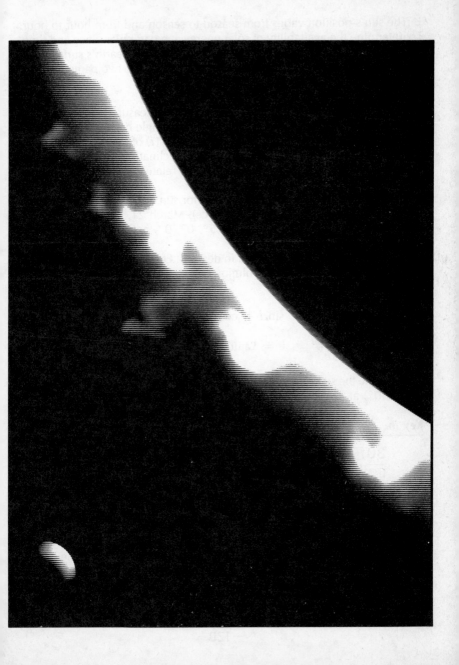

Solar Energy

The sun's position varies from season to season and from hour to hour. To determine the availability of solar energy at a particular place and time, the position of the sun is required. At any point on the earth's surface, sun position is defined by the azimuth and the altitude. The two parameters are related to the latitude, date, and the hour.

The azimuth (z) is the angle of the sun's path measured from the North axis. The altitude (h) is the vertically measured angle between the sun and the plane of the horizon. The angle of incidence (i) of the sun on a flat surface is the complement of the altitude. The declination angle (d) changes with the date because the position of the sun relative to the earth changes.

The extreme and the mean conditions for sun angles occur on the critical dates of December 22 (winter solstice), March 21, September 23, and June 22. The angles would be $-23.5°$, $0°$, $0°$, and $23.5°$ respectively.

The time of day (t) is expressed in degrees. Each hour of the 24 in a day represents $15°$ ($360°$ in one revolution of the earth). One minute is $15'$ and 1 second $= 15''$. Noon is $0°$.

$$\cos i = \sin h = \sin L \, \sin d + \cos L \, \cos d \, \cos t$$

$$\sin Z = \frac{\sin t \, \cos d}{\cos h} \qquad L = \text{Latitude}$$

Calculate the sun's azimuth and angle of incidence on March 21, at 10:00 A.M. ($30°$) at $30°$ South latitude.

Key in: **Answer:**

30 [+/−] [sin] [×] 0 [sin] [+] 30 [+/−] [cos] [×] 0
[cos] [×] 30 [cos] [=] [Min]
[sin⁻¹] $h = 48.6°$
[MR] [cos⁻¹] $i = 41.4°$
30 [sin] [×] 0 [cos] [ )] [÷] 48.6 [cos] [=] [sin⁻¹] $z = 49.1°$

In this case the azimuth has to be between $90°$ and $180°$ and the answer is $130.9°$. The optimum tilt of a solar collector at the above specifications can be calculated from the equation:

Solar Energy

$$0.667 \left(\tan^{-1} \left[\frac{\tan h}{\tan z} \right] - 30° \right)$$

Key in: **Answer:**

48.6 $\boxed{\text{tan}}$ $\boxed{÷}$ **49.1** $\boxed{\text{tan}}$ $\boxed{)}$ $\boxed{\text{tan}^{-1}}$ $\boxed{-}$ **30** $\boxed{)}$ $\boxed{×}$
.667 $\boxed{=}$ **9.67°**

Solar energy is transmitted through the collector surface to an absorbing material. The refractive index of the glass used and the angle of incidence of the sun are the most important factors effecting the radiation transmitted. The fresnel equation takes into account the reflectance from a plate of glass as it varies with the incidence angle.

$$\frac{1}{2} \left[\frac{\sin^2(i - ra)}{\sin^2(i + ra)} + \frac{\tan^2(i - ra)}{\tan^2(i + ra)} \right]$$

The refractive index of glass is 1.52 and $r_a = \sin^{-1} (\sin i/1.52)$.

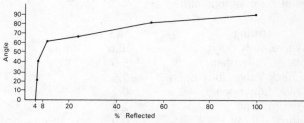

Figure 30: % Reflected

Key in: **Answer:**

for 5°: **5** $\boxed{\text{sin}}$ $\boxed{÷}$ **1.52** $\boxed{)}$ $\boxed{\text{sin}^{-1}}$ $\boxed{\text{M in}}$
   5 $\boxed{-}$ $\boxed{\text{MR}}$ $\boxed{)}$ $\boxed{\text{sin}}$ $\boxed{x^2}$ $\boxed{÷}$ $\boxed{(}$ **5** $\boxed{+}$ $\boxed{\text{MR}}$ $\boxed{)}$ $\boxed{\text{sin}}$ $\boxed{x^2}$
   $\boxed{+}$ $\boxed{(}$ **5** $\boxed{-}$ $\boxed{\text{MR}}$ $\boxed{)}$ $\boxed{\text{tan}}$ $\boxed{x^2}$ $\boxed{÷}$ $\boxed{(}$ **5** $\boxed{+}$ $\boxed{\text{MR}}$ $\boxed{)}$
   $\boxed{\text{tan}}$ $\boxed{x^2}$ $\boxed{)}$ $\boxed{×}$ **.5** $\boxed{=}$ **0.04258 or 4.26%**

for 20°:   **0.04285 or 4.29%**
for 40°:   **0.04845 or 4.85%**
for 60°:   **0.09248 or 9.25%**
for 80°:   **0.39095 or 39.09%**
for 90°:   **1. or 100%**

Fluid Flow

The head, or pressure, lost in transferring a fluid through a conduit has three components: the loss due to a change in elevation, the pressure head, and the velocity head. The generalized equation for total head is:

$$H = Za + \frac{Pa}{W} + \frac{Va^2}{2g}$$

where:
$$
\begin{aligned}
Za &= \text{elevation change} \\
Pa &= \text{pressure, psf} \\
W &= \text{specific weight of fluid, } \#/f^3 \\
Va &= \text{Velocity, } f/s \\
g &= 32.2 \text{ ft/sec/sec}
\end{aligned}
$$

The velocity head may include the head loss due to fittings.

$$h_L = \frac{KV^2}{2g}$$

The values of K for various fittings are:

fitting	K
Globe Valve, fully open	10.0
Angle Valve, fully open	5.0
Swing Check Valve, fully open	2.5
Gate Valve, fully open	0.2
Closed-return bend	2.2
Short-radius* Elbow	0.9
Long-radius* Elbow	0.6
45° Elbow	0.4

* for Short $r/D = 1.0$, for long r/D where:

r = radius of bend
D = pipe diameter

Water flowing at a pressure of 50 psf, a velocity of 60 feet/sec., passes a 45° elbow and a fully open gate valve as it rises 10 feet. What is the loss in head?

Fluid Flow

Key in: **Answer:**

$$10 \boxed{+} 50 \boxed{+} \boxed{(} 1 \boxed{+} .2 \boxed{+} .4 \boxed{)} \boxed{\times}$$
$$60 \boxed{x^2} \boxed{\div} 64.4 \boxed{=}$$ **149.4 feet**

Empirical formulas for head loss state:

$$H = \frac{(20.83/C)^{1.85} \times Q^{1.85}}{D^{4.8655}}$$

> where: D = inside diameter
> C = type of pipe
> Q = flow, gpm

If D = 3/4 inches and C = 130 (for copper pipe), calculate the head loss for the pipe if water is flowing through at 90 gallons per minute.

Key in: **Answer:**

$$20.83 \boxed{\div} 130 \boxed{)} \boxed{x^y} 1.85 \boxed{\times} 90 \boxed{x^y}$$
$$1.85 \boxed{)} \boxed{\div} 3 \boxed{a\%} 4 \boxed{x^y} 4.8655 \boxed{=}$$ **564.96 feet**

Rectangular Ducts

Rectangular ducts are commonly used in heating, ventilating, and air conditioning. Formulas for losses in pressure due to friction are based on circular ducts. The formula for the circular equivalent of a rectangular duct for equal friction and capacity is:

where: a = length of 1 side
b = length of adjacent side

$$dc = 1.3 \sqrt[8]{\frac{(ab)^5}{(a+b)^2}}$$

Calculate for 15 inches and 8 inches and 82,28.

Key in:	*Answer:*
8 $\boxed{\times}$ 15 $\boxed{)}$ $\boxed{x^y}$ 5 $\boxed{\div}$ $\boxed{(}$ 8 $\boxed{+}$ 15	
$\boxed{)}$ $\boxed{x^2}$ $\boxed{)}$ $\boxed{x^{1/3}}$ 8 $\boxed{=}$ $\boxed{\times}$ 1.3 $\boxed{=}$	**11.83 inches**
82 $\boxed{\times}$ 28 $\boxed{)}$ $\boxed{x^y}$ 5 $\boxed{\div}$ $\boxed{(}$ 82 $\boxed{+}$ 28	
$\boxed{)}$ $\boxed{x^2}$ $\boxed{)}$ $\boxed{x^{1/3}}$ 8 $\boxed{=}$ $\boxed{\times}$ 1.3 $\boxed{=}$	**50.606 inches**

Chapter 6 **Financial**

Loans
Amortization
Depreciation

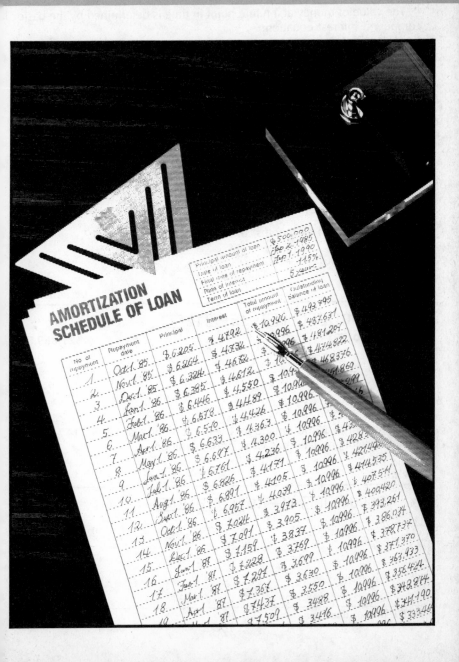

Loans

The value of money at a future point in time is determined by the basic compound interest equation:

$$FV = PV (1 + i)^n$$

where:
PV = Present value
i = interest rate
n = number of periods
FV = Future Value

A computer store buys $20,000 worth of inventory by "Floorplanning" whereby the first 2 months are interest free. The equipment is sold and paid for after 8 months at an interest rate of 18%. Calculate the total paid to the finance company.

$$n = 8 - 2 = 6$$

Note: If n is given as months, then i must be divided by 12.

$$FV = 20,000 (1 + .18/12)^6$$

Key in:	Answer:
20000 $\boxed{\times}$ $\boxed{(}$ 1 $\boxed{+}$ .18 $\boxed{\div}$ 12 $\boxed{)}$ $\boxed{x^y}$ 6 $\boxed{=}$	**$21,868.87**

$$PV = \frac{FV}{(1 + i)^n}$$

A payment of $5,000 made in 4 years at an annual rate of 14%, compounded semi-annually has what present value?

Key in:	Answer:
5000 $\boxed{\div}$ $\boxed{(}$ 1 $\boxed{+}$ .07 $\boxed{)}$ $\boxed{x^y}$ 8 $\boxed{=}$	**$2910.04**

Loans

Interest rates are usually stated on an annual basis — nominal rate of interest. Compounding of interest on a basis other than once a year will result in an effective rate higher than the nominal rate. For continuous compounding the effective rate is:

$$(e^{(\text{nominal rate} \div 100)} - 1) \times 100$$

Calculate the effective continuous rate for 18%.

Key in: **Answer:**

$$18 \boxed{\div} 100 \boxed{)} \boxed{e^x} \boxed{-} 1 \boxed{)} \boxed{\times} 100 \boxed{=}$$ **19.72%**

The interest rate on a loan can be determined from the equation:

$$\text{Interest Rate (\%)} = \frac{2NI}{P(n+1)}$$

where: N = number of payments/year
I = interest paid
P = loan principal
n = total number of payments

A 60-month loan for $100,000 requires a monthly payment of 2,500. What is the annual percentage rate?

$$I = 2,500 \times 60 - 100,000 = 50,000$$

Key in: **Answer:**

$$2 \boxed{\times} 12 \boxed{\times} 50000 \boxed{\div} \boxed{(} 1 \boxed{\text{EXP}} 5 \boxed{\times}$$
$$61 \boxed{=}$$ **0.19672 or 19.67%**

Amortization

On most longer term loans like mortgages and automobile loans, the loan is amortized by the payment of the same amount per month over a specified period of time. The monthly payment includes a small (at first) principal amount and interest. The payment is calculated by the equation:

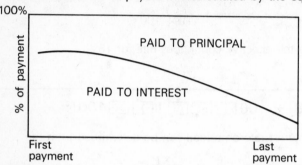

Figure 31: Distribution of Payment between Interest and Principal Over Loan Period

$$\text{Payment} = PV \div \left[\frac{1 - (1 + i)^{-n}}{i} \right]$$

A computer store buys a $12,000 van for delivering systems. A down payment of $1000 is made and arrangements are made to pay off the remainder at an interest rate of 13.5% over a 5-year period. Calculate the monthly payment.

$$n = 5 \times 12 = 60 \qquad\qquad i = .135/12$$

Key in:	*Answer:*
1 ⊟ ⦗ 1 ⊞ .135 ÷ 12 ⦘ x^y 60 +/− ⦘ ÷ ⦗ .135 ÷ 12 = 1/x × 11000 =	**$253.11**

Calculate the total interest paid over the five years:

Key in:	*Answer:*
253.11 × 60 ⊟ 11000 =	**$4186.60**

Amortization

Create an amortization schedule:

First Month:

Key in:		Answer:
Interest:	11000 ☒ .135 ÷ 12 ⊜	$123.75
Principal:	253.11 ⊝ 123.75 ⊜	129.36
Remaining Loan:	11000 ⊝ 129.36 ⊜	10870.64
Second Month:	☒ .135 ÷ 12 ⊜	122.29

Schedule:

Month	Principal Paid	Interest Paid	Remaining Loan
1	$129.36	123.75	10870.64
2	$130.82	122.29	10739.82
etc.			

Depreciation

The Computer Store intends to invest $20,000 in new fixtures with an estimated life of 5 years. Compare the depreciation write off each year using the Accelerated Cost Recovery System (ACRS) of the IRS tax codes versus the sum-of-the years digits technique.

The ACRS on a five year property is 15% the first year, 22% the second, and 21% 3 through 5.

Key in: **Answer:**

Key in	Answer	Year
20000 [X] [X] 15 [%]	3000	1
22 [%]	4400	2
21 [%]	4200	3,4,5
[X] 3 [=]	12600	
Total	20000	

In the sum-of-the years digits method, the number of years is first added up:

$5 + 4 + 3 + 2 + 1 = 15$

Depreciation for the first year is taken as 5/15 of the cost; for the second year as 4/15; and so forth. Use 1/15 of the cost as a constant.

Key in: **Answer:**

20000 [÷] 15 [=]   1333.3333

Key in	Answer	Year
[X] [X] 5 [=] [Min]	$6666.67	1
4 [M+]	5333.33	2
3 [M+]	4000.00	3
2 [M+]	2666.67	4
1 [M+]	1333.33	5
[MR]	20000	

The second technique provides a significally faster write off of an asset.

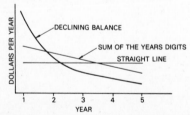

Figure 32: Three Depreciation Techniques compared

Chapter 1 **Technique**

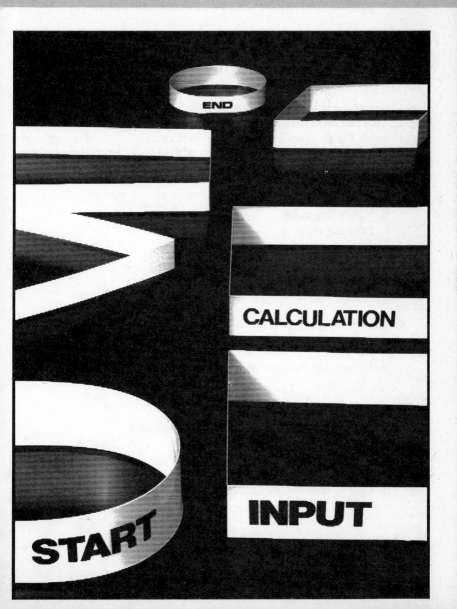

Technique

Some scientific calculators have programmable functions. Before starting to program, the user looks at the problem from five points of view.

A. How can this problem be defined in mathematical terms?

To program the problem, the user must clearly state the situation, the required end result, and the accuracy desired.

B. What method of solution will be used?

After defining the problem, the user selects the optimum method of solution. Many problems have more than one possible solution. The order selected to solve the problem is called an algorithm.

The algorithm for solving the problem of the energy equivalence of one gram of mass where $E = mC^2$ is:

    A. Take the speed of light
    B. Square the value
    C. Take the mass
    D. Multiply "C" by "B"
    E. Display the results

C. What is the logical flow of programming sequences?

The flow of programming sequences is demonstrated by the use of a flowchart. Standard shapes for flowcharting have been developed. They are:

    1. To indicate the start and end of the program ... the oval:

    2. Data is input or output ... the parallelogram:

    3. Data is operated on (multiplication, division, etc.) ... the rectangle:

Technique

4. Decision will be made, followed by branching ... the rhombus:

For $E = mC^2$

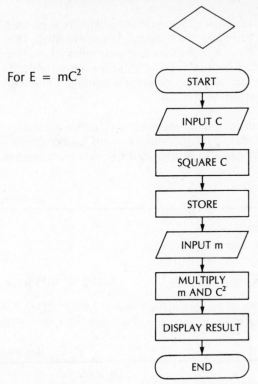

D. How is the problem coded for execution?

Coding is the translating of the logical flow into a detailed set of instructions in the language of the calculator. Coding technique depends on the device used and in computers on the "language" available. Programmable calculator coding is discussed in the following section.

E. How is the coded program tested and checked out?

Use test data with a known answer to the problem to check out the program (debugging). Document your work showing the "key in" format and describing each variable.

PART III: Programming Notes

Technique

Programmable Calculator Techniques

The programmable calculator allows 38 program steps which can be divided into two areas, P1 and P2. To key in a program, change to Mode **LRN**. The flashing P1P2 indicates that now is the time to choose whether you want to program in area P1 or P2. Choose P1. Press ENT for each variable. Always enter a value for the variable when entering a formula. Otherwise, inadvertent "divide by 0" errors may occur.

Note: *Calculators with special registers for constants (k) can help conserve programming space. Before programming $E = mC^2$, store C in K1. The constant registers can also be used to move data from one program to another.*

Key in: **Answer:**

299792458 Kin **1**

For $E = mC^2$ (m is in Kilograms)
Mode: LRN

P1 Kout 1 x^2 ✕ ENT .001 ═ 8.988×10^{13} Joules

Upon completing entering of the formula, change to Mode. (RUN) The program can now be run for many values of m. Try .002, .003, and .010.

Key in: **Answer:**

Mode: RUN

P1 .002 RUN 1.798×10^{14}
P1 .003 RUN 2.696×10^{14}
P1 .010 RUN 8.988×10^{14}

Programs in both P1 and P2 can be erased by using PCL .
Add the conversion to electron volts in P2.

Add: Kin 3 to the program in P1.

Key in: **Answer:**

1.6021892 EXP **19** +/− Kin **2**
Mode: LRN

P2 Kout 3 ÷ Kout 2 ═

PART III: Programming Notes

Technique

Calculate E for .003 m in electron volts.

Key in: *Answer:*

Mode: RUN

$\boxed{P_1}$ .003 $\boxed{\text{RUN}}$ $\boxed{P_2}$ $\boxed{\text{RUN}}$ $1.683 \times 10^{33} e$V

The answer in joules may also be shown before the answer in electron volts within the same program by using the "halt" command. The program is:

Key in: *Answer:*

Mode: LRN

$\boxed{P_1}$ $\boxed{\text{Kout}}$ 1 $\boxed{x^2}$ $\boxed{\times}$ $\boxed{\text{ENT}}$ .001 $\boxed{=}$ $\boxed{\text{HLT}}$ $\boxed{\div}$ $\boxed{\text{Kout}}$ 2 $\boxed{=}$
$\boxed{\text{MODE}}$ $\boxed{\;\cdot\;}$ $\boxed{P_1}$

    .002 $\boxed{\text{RUN}}$ 1.798×10^{14} **Joules**
            $\boxed{\text{RUN}}$ 1.122×10^{33} eV

The command "**RETURN**" permits calculation with a series of values. Add "**RTN**" to the original program.
Programs using $\boxed{\text{RTN}}$ must begin with $\boxed{\text{ENT}}$. To stop the program use $\boxed{\text{AC}}$.

Key in: *Answer:*

Mode: LRN

$\boxed{P_1}$ $\boxed{\text{ENT}}$ .001 $\boxed{\times}$ $\boxed{\text{Kout}}$ 1 $\boxed{x^2}$ $\boxed{=}$ $\boxed{\text{RTN}}$

Mode: RUN

$\boxed{P_1}$ .001 $\boxed{\text{RUN}}$ .002 $\boxed{\text{RUN}}$ .003 $\boxed{\text{RUN}}$ $\boxed{\text{AC}}$

Chapter 2 **Math**

$$\int_a^b f(x)\,dx$$

Quadratic Equation

To program the quadratic equation solution:

Key in:	*Notes:*
Mode: LRN	
$\boxed{P_1}$ $\boxed{ENT}$ 3 $\boxed{K\,in}$ 1 $\boxed{x^2}$ $\boxed{-}$ 4 $\boxed{\times}$	**Value of**
$\boxed{ENT}$ 2 $\boxed{K\,in}$ 2 $\boxed{\times}$ $\boxed{ENT}$ 1 $\boxed{)}$ $\boxed{\sqrt{\ }}$	**Discriminant**
$\boxed{K\,in}$ 3	**Stores discriminant**
$\boxed{P_2}$ $\boxed{AC}$	
$\boxed{K\,out}$ 3 $\boxed{-}$ $\boxed{K\,out}$ 1 $\boxed{)}$ $\boxed{\div}$ 2	
$\boxed{\div}$ $\boxed{K\,out}$ 2 $\boxed{=}$ $\boxed{HLT}$	**Root 1**
$\boxed{K\,out}$ 1 $\boxed{+/-}$ $\boxed{-}$ $\boxed{K\,out}$ 3 $\boxed{)}$ $\boxed{\div}$	
2 $\boxed{\div}$ $\boxed{K\,out}$ 2 $\boxed{=}$	**Root 2**

Solve for: $4x^2 + 18x - 8$

Key in:	*Answer:*
Mode: RUN	
$\boxed{P_1}$ 18 $\boxed{RUN}$ 4 $\boxed{RUN}$ 8 $\boxed{+/-}$ $\boxed{RUN}$	
$\boxed{P_2}$	**.4075**
$\boxed{RUN}$	**− 4.908**

Series

Programming is particularly convenient for solving series:

Program and solve the series:

$$\frac{x^3}{3} - \frac{x^7}{7(3!)} + \frac{x^{11}}{11(5!)} - \frac{x^{15}}{15(7!)}$$

Key in: **Answer:**

Mode: LRN

    [P₁] [ENT] 1 [K in] 3

    [P₂] [K out] 3 [xʸ] [( ] [( ] [K out] 1 [+] 4 [ )] [K in] 1 [÷] [( ] [K out]

    1 [×] [( ] [( ] [K out] 2 [+] 2 [ )] [K in] 2 [x!] [=]

Mode: RUN

    initialize: 1 [+/−] [K in] 1 [K in] 2   0 [Min]

    Solve for $x = .5$:

Key in: **Displayed answer:**

    [P₁] .5 [RUN]

    [P₂] [RUN] [M+]   0.041666666

    [P₂] [RUN] [M−] [MR]   0.041480654

    [P₂] [RUN] [M+] [MR]   0.041481024

    [P₂] [RUN] [M−] [MR]   0.041481024

Simpson's Rule

Solving integrals by Simpson's Rule may be programmed on calculators that have the special integral mode $\int dx$.

Solve for $2x^3 + 2.85x^2 - 6.8$ from 3 to 6.
Mode: LRN [P1] [Min]
Key in: ***Answer:***

$$2 \boxed{\times} \boxed{\text{MR}} \boxed{x^y} 3 \boxed{+} 2.85 \boxed{\times} \boxed{\text{MR}} \boxed{x^2} \boxed{-} 6.8 \boxed{=}$$
Mode: $\int dx$
  [P1] 2 [HLT]
  3 [RUN] 6 [RUN]   **766.65**

After carrying out the integration, the calculator stores the related values in the memory registers as follows:

K out	Function	
1	a	3
2	b	6
3	N	4
4	$f(a)$	72.85
5	$f(b)$	527.8
6	$\int_a^b f(x)\,dx$	766.65

Chapter 3 Finance

Finance

A bond whose present worth is greater than its cost is considered to be a "good" investment. The present worth is determined by adding the present worth of the coupon (interest payment) to the present worth of the payment at maturity of the bond.

$$PW = A \left[\frac{1 - (1 + r)^{-n}}{r} \right] + F/(1 + r)^n$$

Note: *Negative exponents are handled more efficiently by programming the exponent as positive and entering the amount as a negative.*

Key in:

Mode: LRN

[P1] 1 [−] [(] 1 [+] [ENT] 1 [Kin] 1 [)] [x^y] [ENT] 2 [)]
[÷] [Kout] 1 [)] [×] [ENT] 3 [+] [ENT] 4 [÷] [(] 1 [+] [Kout]
1 [)] [x^y] [ENT] 5 [=]

Calculate the present worth of a $10,000 bond discounted 3% paying $1,200 per year for 10 years. The 12% per year payment is made annually.

Mode: RUN			Notes:
[P1]	.12	[RUN]	*Interest Rate*
	10 [+/−]	[RUN]	*Number of Periods*
	1200	[RUN]	*Annual Payment*
	9700	[RUN]	*Bonds Discounted, Current Cost*
	10	[RUN]	*Number of Periods*

Answer:

Note: *Present Worth* **$9903.41**

APPENDIX

I. Calculator Priorities
II. Important Reference Tables

I. Calculator Priorities

The following material is not directly related to operation but is included to help you understand the calculator. The material explains how the calculator accomplishes calculations when the expression is input 'as written'. To do this, the functions of the registers must be explained.

Example of Register Contents

X-register (display)
Y-register (arithmetic operations)
L₁-register
L₂-register
L₃-register
L₄-register
L₅-register
L₆-register

Used in arithmetic and functional calculations.

Used in calculations with nesting parentheses and for judging the precedence of addition/subtraction and multiplication/division.

Calculator priority means that the calculator automatically decides the precedence of ① functional calculations ② power functions, radical roots ③ multiplication and division ④ addition and subtraction, in this order and calculates expressions in parentheses giving the correct precedence to each operation.

I. Calculator Priorities

1. When no precedence of operation is involved

(That is when the calculation can be effected in the order of input.) If $3 + 5 - 2 + 4 =$ were to be calculated for example, this is what happens in the register.

Operation		3	⊞	5	⊟	2	⊞	4	⊟
register	X	3	3	5	8	2	6	4	10 ←
	Y	0	3 +	3 +	8 −	8 −	6 +	6 +	0
	L₁	0	0	0	0	0	0	0	0
	L₂	0	0	0	0	0	0	0	0
	L₃	0	0	0	0	0	0	0	0
	L₄	0	0	0	0	0	0	0	0
	L₅	0	0	0	0	0	0	0	0
	L₆	0	0	0	0	0	0	0	0

fact that

- The content of the X register is what is shown in the display and can thus be verified.
- The content of the Y register is inside the calculator but can be verified by pushing the [X↔Y] key.
* 0 means that the register is clear.

Thus for calculations containing only addition and subtraction or only multiplication and division, however long the expression is, only the two registers X (display) and Y (calculation) are used.

I. Calculator Priorities

2. When precedence of operation is involved

In expressions such as $7 \times 4 + \underset{\sim\sim\sim}{3 \times 5} - \underset{\sim\sim\sim}{16 \div 2}$ calculation of the underlined part takes precedence.

Operation	① 7	② ⊠	③ 4	④ ⊞	⑤ 3	⑥ ⊠	⑦ 5	⑧ ⊟	⑨ 16	⑩ ⊞	⑪ 2	⑫ ⊟
register X	7	7	4	28	3	3	5	43	16	16	2	35
Y	0	7 x	7 x	28+	28+	3 x	3 x	43−	43−	16÷	16÷	0
L_1	0	0	0	0	0	28+	28+	0	0	43−	43−	0
L_2	0	0	0	0	0	0	0	0	0	0	0	0
L_3	0	0	0	0	0	0	0	0	0	0	0	0
L_4	0	0	0	0	0	0	0	0	0	0	0	0
L_5	0	0	0	0	0	0	0	0	0	0	0	0
L_6	0	0	0	0	0	0	0	0	0	0	0	0

In the above example, in the ⊠ operation of step ⑥ and the ⊞ operation of step ⑩, the value in the Y register is moved to the L_1 register. This is because the ⊠ operation takes precedence over the ⊞ operation of step ④ while ⊞ of step ⑩ takes precedence over ⊟ of step ⑧ and the interim result is kept for later use.

Since ⊟ in step ⑧ is of the same precedence as ⊞ of step ④ operating this key effects an addition of 5×3 and the value in L_1, 28 +, is effected and 43 obtained. Thus, when the expression contains the four fundamental arithmetic operations but not parentheses, however long it may be, at most the L_1 register is used in addition to the X and Y.

I. Calculator Priorities

An example of such an expression is

$$a + b \times c^d =$$

For example in the expression $4 + 5 \times 6^7 =$ the underlined sections take precedence.

Operation		4	$\boxed{+}$	5	$\boxed{\times}$	6	$\boxed{x^y}$	7	$\boxed{=}$
register	X	4	4	5	5	6	6	7	1399684
	Y	0	4+	4+	5×	5×	$6x^y$	$6x^y$	0
	L_1	0	0	0	4+	4+	5×	5×	0
	L_2	0	0	0	0	0	4+	4+	0
	L_3	0	0	0	0	0	0	0	0
	L_4	0	0	0	0	0	0	0	0
	L_5	0	0	0	0	0	0	0	0
	L_6	0	0	0	0	0	0	0	0

As seen above, until the last $\boxed{=}$ is operated, the elements 4 + and 5 × must be separately stored.

* In the above example 6^7 is a power function and thus takes precedence over 5×6^7 which in turn takes precedence over 4 +.

I. Calculator Priorities

3. Calculation of expressions containing parentheses

In such expressions, the precedence of parentheses is also taken into account.

Example: $5 + 4 \times [6 - 7 \times (3 - 2)] =$

Operation		① 5	② [+]	③ 4	④ [×]	⑤ [(]	⑥ 6	⑦ [−]	⑧ 7	⑨ [×]	⑩ [(]	⑪ 3	⑫ [−]	⑬ 2	⑭ [)]	⑮ [)]	⑯ [=]
register	X	5	5	4	4	0	6	6	7	7	0	3	3	2	1	−1	1
	Y	0	5+	5+	4x	0	0	6−	6−	7x	0	0	3−	3−	7x	4x	0
	L_1	0	0	0	5+	(4x	(4x	(4x	(4x	(6−	(7x	(7x	(7x	(7x	(6−	5+	0
	L_2	0	0	0	0	5+	5+	5+	5+	4x	(6−	(6−	(6−	(6−	4x	0	0
	L_3	0	0	0	0	0	0	0	0	5+	4x	4x	4x	4x	5+	0	0
	L_4	0	0	0	0	0	0	0	0	0	5+	5+	5+	5+	0	0	0
	L_5	0	0	0	0	0	0	0	0	0	0	0	0	0	0	0	0
	L_6	0	0	0	0	0	0	0	0	0	0	0	0	0	0	0	0

The reason the registers are used in the above manner can readily be understood by going back to the previous examples.

Strategy: From this example, the fact that the calculator can handle six multiple parentheses can be understood. Also it must be understood that this is the maximum and the real number of parentheses that can be handled depends on the operations for precedence involved.

For both parenthesis and operational precedence, values and operations input first must be stored so that latter input takes precedence. For this reason, registers $L_1 - L_6$ are used for storing values and operations in both parenthesis operations and operational precedence. These six registers assure that all problems can be efficiently handled.

II. Important Reference Tables

Table 1
Metrics & Prefixes

Basic length units

Unit	Conversion factor	Value in meters
Micron	10^{-6}	0.000001
Millimeter	10^{-3}	0.001
Centimeter	10^{-2}	0.01
Decimeter	10^{-1}	0.1
Meter	10^0	1.0
Dekameter	10^1	10.0
Hectometer	10^2	100.0
Kilometer	10^3	1,000.0
Myriameter	10^4	10,000.0
Megameter	10^6	1,000,000.0

Prefixes

Prefix	Conversion factor	Place-name
Exa	10^{18}	
Peta	10^{15}	
Tera	10^{12}	trillions
Giga	10^9	billions
Mega	10^6	millions
Myria	10^4	ten-thousands
Kilo	10^3	thousands
Hecto	10^2	hundreds
Deca	10^1	tens
Basic unit	10^0	ones
Deci	10^{-1}	tenths
Centi	10^{-2}	hundredths
Milli	10^{-3}	thousandths
Micro	10^{-6}	millionths
Nano	10^{-9}	billionths
Pico	10^{-12}	trillionths
Femto	10^{-15}	
Atto	10^{-18}	

II. Important Reference Tables

Table 2
Standard Units of Measurement

Mass: $\quad 1 \text{ Kg} = \dfrac{1}{0.45359237} \text{ lb} = 2.205 \text{ lb}$

Length: $\quad 1 \text{ m} = \dfrac{1}{0.3048} \text{ ft} = 3.281 \text{ ft}$

Volume: $\quad 1 \text{ m}^3 = 35.31 \text{ ft}^3$

Time: $\quad 1 \text{ s} = \dfrac{1}{60} \text{ min} = \dfrac{1}{3600} \text{ hr}$

Temperature: $\quad 1 \text{ K} = 1.8 \text{ R}$

Force: $\quad 1 \text{ N } (\text{kgm/s}^2) = 10^5 \text{ dyn} = 0.2248 \text{ lbf}$

Pressure: $\quad 1 \text{ bar} = 10^5 \text{ N/m}^2 = 14.50 \text{ lbf/in}^2 = 750 \text{ mm Hg} = 10.2 \text{ m H}_2\text{O}$

Specific Volume: $\quad 1 \text{ m}^3/\text{kg} = 16.02 \text{ ft}^3/\text{lb}$

Density: $\quad 1 \text{ kg/m}^3 = 0.06243 \text{ lb/ft}^3$

II. Important Reference Tables

Table 3

Weights and Measures

APOTHECARIES' WEIGHT

20 grains	1 scruple
3 scruples	1 dram
8 drams	1 ounce
12 ounces	1 pound

Ounce and pound are the same as in Troy Weight.

AVOIRDUPOIS WEIGHT

27 11/32 grains	1 dram
16 drams	1 ounce
16 ounces	1 pound
25 pounds	1 quarter
4 quarters	1 cwt.
2,000 pounds	1 short ton
2,240 pounds	1 long ton

TROY WEIGHT

24 grains	1 pwt.
20 pwt.	1 ounce
12 ounces	1 pound

Used for weighing gold, silver and jewels.

CLOTH MEASURE

2¼ inches	1 nail
4 nails	1 quarter
4 quarters	1 yard

CUBIC MEASURE

1,728 cubic inches	1 cubic foot
27 cubic feet	1 cubic yard
128 cubic feet	1 cord (wood)
40 cubic feet	1 ton (shipping)
2,150.42 cubic inches	1 standard bu.
231 cubic inches	1 U.S. standard gal.
1 cubic foot	about 4/5 of a bushel

DRY MEASURE

2 pints	1 quart
8 quarts	1 peck
4 pecks	1 bushel
36 bushels	1 chaldron

LIQUID MEASURE

4 gills	1 pint
2 pints	1 quart
4 quarts	1 gallon
31½ gallons	1 barrel
2 barrels	1 hogshead

LONG MEASURE

12 inches	1 foot
3 feet	1 yard
5½ yards	1 rod
40 rods	1 furlong
8 furlongs	1 sta. mile
3 miles	1 league

MARINERS' MEASURE

6 feet	1 fathom
120 fathoms	1 cable length
7½ cable lengths	1 mile
5,280 feet	1 statute mile
6,080.2 feet	1 nautical mile

SQUARE MEASURE

144 sq. inches	1 sq. ft.
9 sq. ft.	1 sq. yard
30¼ sq. yards	1 sq. rod
40 sq. rods	1 rood
4 roods	1 acre
640 acres	1 sq. mile

SURVEYORS' MEASURE

7.92 inches	1 link
25 links	1 rod
4 rods	1 chain
10 sq. chains or 160 sq. rods	1 acre
640 acres	1 sq. mile
36 sq. miles (6 miles sq.)	1 township

TIME MEASURE

60 seconds	1 minute
60 minutes	1 hour
24 hours	1 day
7 days	1 week
28, 29, 30 or 31 days	1 cal. month
30 days	1 month ... in comp. interest
365 days	1 year ... 366 days 1 lp. yr.

MISCELLANEOUS

3 inches	1 palm
4 inches	1 hand
6 inches	1 span
18 inches	1 cubit
21.8 inches	1 Bible cubit
2½ feet	1 military pace

II. Important Reference Tables

METRIC EQUIVALENTS
Linear Measure

1 centimeter	0.3937 inches
1 inch	2.54 centimeters
1 decimeter	3.937 in.... 0.328 foot
1 foot	3.048 decimeters
1 meter	39.37 inches ... 1.09.36 yds.
1 yard	0.9144 meter
1 dekameter	1.9884 rods
1 rod	0.5029 dekameter
1 kilometer	0.621.37 mile
1 mile	1.609.3 kilometers

Square Measure

1 square centimeter	0.1550 sq. inches
1 square inch	6.452 square centimeters
1 square decimeter	0.1076 square foot
1 square foot	9.2903 square dec.
1 square meter	1.196 square yds.
1 square yard	0.8361 square meter
1 acre	160 square rods
1 square rod	0.00625 acre
1 hectare	2.47 acres
1 acre	0.4047 hectare
1 square kilometer	0.386 sq. mile
1 square mile	2.59 sq. kilometers

Measure of Volume

1 cubic centimeter	0.061 cu. inch
1 cubic inch	16.39 cubic cent.
1 cubic decimeter	0.0353 cubic foot
1 cubic foot	28.317 cubic dec.
1 cubic meter	1.308 cubic yards
1 cubic yard	0.7646 cubic meter
1 stere	0.2759 cord
1 cord	3.624 steres
1 liter	0.908 qt. dry ... 1.0567 qts. liq.
1 quart dry	1.101 liters
1 quart liquid	0.9463 liter
1 dekaliter	2.6417 gals.... 1.135 pecks
1 gallon	0.3785 dekaliter
1 peck	0.881 dekaliter
1 hektoliter	2.8375 bushels
1 bushel	0.3524 hektoliter

Weights

1 gram	0.03527 ounce
1 ounce	28.35 grams
1 kilogram	2.2046 pounds
1 pound	0.4536 kilogram
1 metric ton	0.98421 English ton
1 English ton	1.016 metric ton

APPROXIMATE METRIC EQUIVALENTS

1 decimeter	4 inches
1 liter	1.06 quarts liquid, 0.9 qt. dry
1 meter	1.1 yards
1 kilometer	⅝ of a mile
1 hektoliter	2⅝ bushels
1 hectare	2½ acres
1 kilogram	2⅕ pounds
1 stere, or cubic meter	¼ of a cord
1 metric ton	2,204.6 pounds

TEMPERATURES

	Fahrenheit
Milk	Freezes 30° above Zero
Water	Freezes 32° above Zero
Olive Oil	Freezes 36° above Zero
Wines	Freezes 20° above Zero
Vinegar	Freezes 28° above Zero
Alcohol	Boils at 173° above Zero
Water	Boils at 212° above Zero
Petrol. (av.)	Boils at 360° above Zero
Blood Heat	98.4° above Zero
Eggs Hatch	104° above Zero

II. Important Reference Tables

Table 4
Physical Constants

Mechanical

Universal Gravitation $\quad G = 6.672 \times 10^{-11}$ N$-$m^2/Kg^2

Thermodynamic

Boltzmann Constant $\quad k = 1.3807 \times 10^{-23}$ J/K

Gas Constant $\quad R = 8.314$ J/mol$-$K

Avogadro's Number $\quad N_A = 6.022 \times 10^{23}$/mol

Stefan-Boltzmann Constant $\quad \sigma = 5.670 \times 10^{-8}$ W/m$^2-$K^4

Ideal Gas Volume at STP $\quad V_o = 22.4136$ liters/mol

Electrical

Electric Constant $\quad K_e = 8.9876 \times 10^9$ N$-$m^2/C^2

Magnetic Constant $\quad K_m = 1.000 \times 10^{-7}$ N/A$-$m

Electric Charge $\quad e = 1.602 \times 10^{-19}$ C

Faraday Constant $\quad F = N_A e = 9.648 \times 10^4$ C/mol

Speed of Light $\quad c = 2.9979 \times 10^8$ m/s

Atomic

Planck's Constant $\quad h = 6.626 \times 10^{-34}$ J$-$s

Bohr Radius $\quad a_o = 5.292 \times 10^{-11}$ m

Atomic Mass Unit $\quad 1\ amu = 1.6606 \times 10^{-27}$ Kg $= 931.5$ MeV/c^2

Electron Mass $\quad M_e = 9.1095 \times 10^{-31}$ Kg $= 0.5110$ MeV/c^2

Proton Mass $\quad m_p = 1.6726 \times 10^{-27}$ Kg $= 938.28$ MeV/c^2

Neutron Mass $\quad m_n = 1.6750 \times 10^{-27}$ Kg $= 939.57$ MeV/c^2

Electron Volt $\quad 1\ e$V$ = 1.602 \times 10^{-19}$ J

II. Important Reference Tables

Table 5

United States Standard Gage Sizes
For Sheet and Plate Iron and Steel

Number of Gage	Approximate Thickness, Inches, (Fractions)	Approximate Thickness, Inches, (Decimals)	Weight per Square Foot, Pounds, Avoirdupois
0000000	1/2	.5	20.00
000000	15/32	.4688	18.75
00000	7/16	.4375	17.50
0000	13/32	.4063	16.25
000	3/8	.375	15.00
00	11/32	.3438	13.75
0	5/16	.3125	12.50
1	9/32	.2813	11.25
2	17/64	.2656	10.625
3	1/4	.25	10.00
4	15/64	.2344	9.375
5	7/32	.2188	8.75
6	13/64	.2031	8.125
7	3/16	.1875	7.5
8	11/64	.1719	6.875
9	5/32	.1563	6.25
10	9/64	.1406	5.625
11	1/8	.125	5.00
12	7/64	.1094	4.375
13	3/32	.0938	3.75
14	5/64	.0781	3.125
15	9/128	.0703	2.8125
16	1/16	.0625	2.5
17	9/160	.0563	2.25
18	1/20	.05	2.
19	7/160	.0438	1.75
20	3/80	.0375	1.50
21	11/320	.0344	1.375
22	1/32	.0313	1.25
23	9/320	.0281	1.125
24	1/40	.025	1.
25	7/320	.0219	.875
26	3/160	.0188	.75
27	11/640	.0172	.6875
28	1/64	.0156	.625
29	9/640	.0141	.5625
30	1/80	.0125	.5
31	7/640	.0109	.4375
32	13/1280	.0102	.4063
33	3/320	.0094	.375
34	11/1280	.0086	.3438
35	5/640	.0078	.3125
36	9/1280	.0070	.2813
37	17/2560	.0066	.2656
38	1/160	.0063	.25

INDEX